ADOPTING A CHILD LIVING WITH FETAL ALCOHOL SPECTRUM DISORDER

By Liz Lawryk BSW MSc. H.S. RSW

Library and Archives Canada Cataloguing in Publication

Lawryk, Liz 1959 -

Adopting a Child Living with Fetal Alcohol Spectrum Disorder / Liz Lawryk; edited by Karen D. Crowdis ... [et. al.]

Includes bibliographical references, glossary, and index.

ISBN 978-0-973 7739-1-0

1. Fetal Alcohol Spectrum Disorder 2. Adoption 3. Adopting a Child with FASD 3.Children with Developmental Disabilities. I. Crowdis, Karen D. 1968.04.21. Title.

Edited by: Karen D. Crowdis

Published by the **OBD** Triage Institute Inc., Bragg Creek, (Calgary) Alberta, Canada.

Printed by Rhino Print, Calgary, Alberta, Canada.

Design by Spindrift Design Studio Inc.

Special Thanks to Contributors:

Tracy Breher, Mary Jane and Ed Claussen, Alison Farrell, Robin Hilborn, Sharon and Ray Joyal, Heather Hayes, Jodee Kulp, Sue Roughley, Carol Soby, Melanie Wagstaff, and Ann Yurcek.

Special acknowledgement and thanks to Myles Himmelreich, Liz Kulp, Justin Schafer, and Katei S. for their participation, suggestions, inspiration, and courage to share their stories.

We learn the most from you.

Thank you to the countless parents, and individuals who have shared their experiences for the benefit of other families and professional education.

To my Editor Karen Crowdis—thank you for your insight and thoughtfulness.

Wolf Wolfensberger, PhD (1934-2011)

Dr. Wolfensberger was an originator of Social Role Valorization and the Normalization Principle, concepts that strongly influenced disability policy and practice in Canada, the United States, Australia, Europe, and the United Kingdom. He was an early leader in promoting deinstitutionalization, integration, the development of comprehensive community services and family advocacy. His life's work strongly influenced my personal and professional goals. I am eternally grateful for his contributions.

Adopting a Child Living with Fetal Alcohol Spectrum Disorder

Introduction

Fetal Alcohol Spectrum Disorder (FASD) has a lengthy history of being the most misunderstood form of organic brain injury in our society today. This medical disposition is one of the most complex and variable forms of permanent brain dysfunction, and is often described in literature or websites with the focus on "behaviour problems" or faint hope for a successful future.

Early on in my work with adoptive families a common theme appeared. Many families had children come to them with little to no information about the possibility the child would have Fetal Alcohol Spectrum Disorder or, what it meant. That was three decades ago and unfortunately, this still occurs today.

Certainly in years past, this was because there was little to no information available regarding FASD in general. Parents were not prepared for the intricacies of Fetal Alcohol Spectrum Disorder, what to expect, or how to manage a child or teen with an often undiagnosed medical concern.

In some circumstances adoptive parents have shared, "If we knew what our lives were going to be like with this child, we would never have adopted." These parents were not heartless, self-centred, uneducated people. They *did not have all the necessary information* that we have today in order to make an informed decision. Further, professionals and support services agencies were not available and/or specifically trained in knowing how to appropriately provide assistance. In some cases, families made the devastating decision to give the child back to Social Services or to the child's country of origin. They simply didn't know what to expect, were ill equipped, and lacked the range of specialised resources and supports to help guide them.

The first FASD Diagnostic Clinic began in 1993 in Seattle at the University of Washington, U.S.A.[1] Regardless, Provincial and State FASD Diagnostic Clinics have only been established in Canada and the U.S. in approximately the last 10 years. In some countries, it is still not considered an important medical issue. Secondly, helping professionals, Social Services and community agencies were not yet well informed in the multifaceted factors surrounding the *whole body disorder as a medical diagnosis*. Therefore, support services struggled in knowing how or what to provide children, youth, and families living with suspected or diagnosed FASD.

More recently, a wealth of detailed information regarding FASD has become available. Existing FASD Diagnostic Clinics have had some time to review and follow up with individuals that have been medically diagnosed. Continuing research in all components of FASD has strengthened our knowledge base and families have contributed by sharing their experiences of raising children with or suspected to have FASD. Most impressive is the number of adults living successfully with a diagnosis within Fetal Alcohol Spectrum Disorder that are willing to share their life experiences to further educate us in how to best support them and their peers of any age.

Adopting any child involves the readiness to learn everything you can about *all* of their prospective needs. In doing so, you and your family can determine whether you are suited to raising a child or youth with issues likely greater than many other children. It is anticipated that some people who read this book will decide not to adopt a child with FASD while others will still adopt. Either way, the objective of this guidebook is to give you medically accurate, fair and balanced answers to your questions. It is possible to lessen the impact of a child's biological risks by providing a nurturing, receptive, and healthy environment. Nevertheless, love alone is not enough. While you read through this book, consider whether you can relate to some of the identified issues. Ask yourself some questions. Do some of the same issues occur in your own life? Do you ever forget things? How does it feel when you cannot remember something? Is there someone in your life right now that just will not do what you want them to do, when you want them to do it? How do you deal with that? Could you live with a person that has severe Alzheimer's disease that has sporadic memory loss, needs constant supervision, whose behaviour is completely inconsistent and unpredictable? How would you feel in their situation?

All of us can relate to having differences in the way we think, learn, and manage ourselves. People living with FASD simply experience them more often and with more intensity. Looking at the world from their perspective and more importantly, how the world sees them may give you the clarity you are looking for. It is hopeful that with this information, you will discover whether you may be the right family for a child or teen living with Fetal Alcohol Spectrum Disorder.

Chapter One

Fetal Alcohol Spectrum Disorders: The Basics

In this chapter we will discuss what Fetal Alcohol Spectrum Disorders (FASD) are, how they are caused, and alcohol and drugs' potential effects on the brain and body.

What is Fetal Alcohol Spectrum Disorder?

Fetal Alcohol Spectrum Disorder (FASD) is an umbrella term describing a range of effects that can occur in an individual whose mother drank alcohol during pregnancy. This may include physical abnormalities, sensory integration variables (how we "filter and feel" information), learning disabilities and/or behavioural issues with lifelong implications.

It is referred to as organic brain injury because it was caused by something (such as alcohol, virus, or a DNA issue) that altered the normal development of the fetus during pregnancy.

Diagnoses within FASD are *medical diagnoses*, not a psychiatric or psychological disorder. As it encompasses the entire body, including the brain, it is considered a whole body disorder.

It is a permanent brain injury/dysfunction that the child will not "grow out of."

How is Fetal Alcohol Spectrum Disorder Caused?

Fetal Alcohol Spectrum Disorders are caused by a woman drinking alcohol during pregnancy. Not all individuals with prenatal alcohol exposure are necessarily affected, but many have physical, intellectual, and/or sensory complications and as a result, behavioural issues.

Women do not intentionally set out to drink alcohol while pregnant. Many women who confirmed drinking during pregnancy also disclosed that they were sexually, physically and/or emotionally abused as children. Childhood maltreatment often results in addiction to alcohol and/or drugs.

In many cases, women *do not know* that they are pregnant when they are drinking. For example, a college student that is not aware she is pregnant may be studying for exams and is not drinking alcohol. After writing her exams she celebrates by drinking alcohol with her friends not knowing that alcohol could be harming her baby.

Some women may experience menstrual spotting due to a number of causes including being pregnant, taking birth control pills, hormone imbalance, infection, medications, polyps, dysplasia (a slightly more serious condition in which tissue cells mature abnormally) and cervical cancer. These could lead to a false sense of security that drinking alcohol at that time would be inconsequential.

There are countless variations from woman to woman in how much alcohol is consumed, at what stage of the pregnancy, the mother's overall health and how her body processes alcohol. As a result, *no two prenatally exposed individuals are ever identical physically, intellectually, how they perceive sensations, or behaviourally,* even though they may have the same terminology of medical diagnosis.

Myths and Facts

Myth: The father's alcohol use prior to conception may damage his sperm and result in the baby having FASD.

Fact: The *only way* a fetus can be affected by alcohol is if the **biological mother** consumes alcohol during the pregnancy. Men who drink high volumes of alcohol may risk a lower sperm count and/or slower mobility of their sperm but this has nothing to do with causing FASD.[2,3]

Myth: FASD can be "passed down" through the generations.

Fact: In the case where a woman has a diagnosis within Fetal Alcohol Spectrum Disorder (FASD), and she *does not drink alcohol while she is pregnant*, the baby would not have FASD.

Myth: Children, youth and adults diagnosed within FASD will not finish school, will be alcoholics or drug addicts, and likely end up in jail, or homeless.

Fact: Early literature in the area of FASD cites these concerns. Nonetheless, *early diagnosis* and *patient specific support* clearly reduces the risk of these potential issues. Many adults living with FASD have not experienced these problems and lead successful lives with various types of supports.

Prenatal Alcohol and Drug Use in Pregnancy

Prenatal use of alcohol and/or drugs can cause potential harm to the fetus. "When a pregnant woman drinks, alcohol passes through the placenta to her fetus. In the fetus's immature body, alcohol is broken down much more slowly than in an adult's body. As a result, the alcohol level of the baby's blood can be higher and remain elevated longer than the level in the mother's blood. This sometimes causes the baby to suffer lifelong damage." [4]

Do illegal and prescription drugs have the same effect as alcohol in a pregnancy?

- The current drug (prescription or illegal) that does the most damage to a fetus is Accutane® which is prescribed for acne treatment.

- Other than Accutane®, alcohol still does the most damage within all of the drug groups.

- Anti-seizure medications may cause physical and cognitive differences that mimic FASD in presentation. If a mother takes anticonvulsant medication in her pregnancy, it could result in a diagnosis of Fetal Hydantoin syndrome/effects. [5]

Potential effects of Marijuana use in pregnancy

- Some patients have been found to display altered responses to visual stimulation (they cannot focus or filter light), increased tremors (shaking), and a high-pitched cry (screeching), which may indicate problems with brain (central nervous system) development. Some marijuana-exposed children (preschool and early childhood) have been reported to have more behavioural problems and difficulties with sustained attention and memory than children who were not exposed to marijuana. [6] Davies and Bledsoe (2005) found "no consistent link between prenatal marijuana exposure and other adverse pregnancy outcomes or congenital malformations". [7]

- To date, research is not clear as to whether any effects of marijuana during pregnancy persist as the child grows up; however, because some parts of the brain continue to develop into adolescence, it is also possible that certain kinds of problems will become more evident as the child matures.

Potential Effects of Cocaine use in pregnancy

- The full extent of the effects of prenatal drug exposure on a child is not completely known. Many scientific studies have documented that babies born to mothers who abuse cocaine during pregnancy are often prematurely delivered, have low birth weights, smaller head circumferences, and are often shorter in length. Infants may present as irritable with disrupted sleep patterns. Central Nervous System (CNS) neurological problems could be seizures, tremors or hypertonia (extreme tension of the muscles).

- "Crack babies" born to mothers, who used cocaine while pregnant, were "written off" by many a decade ago as a lost generation. They were predicted to suffer from severe, irreversible damage, including reduced intelligence and social skills. It was later found that this was a gross exaggeration. Most crack-exposed babies appear to recover quite well. However, the fact that most of these children appear normal should not be over-interpreted as a positive sign.[8]

- Further, *it is very possible that a mother who used cocaine in pregnancy may have also used alcohol.* **Caution** – It should be noted that maternal ingestion of substance interviews conducted by the **OBD** (**O**rganic **B**rain **D**ysfunction) Triage Institute since 1989, found that typically, but not exclusively, biological mothers who have confirmed use of substances such as cocaine, crystal methamphetamine, or heroin in pregnancy, are more likely to also use alcohol as well, particularly if the drug is not available.[9]

Even if there is speculation or confirmation that the mother solely used drugs in pregnancy, a full medical evaluation for the possibility of FASD is strongly recommended.

Potential Effects of Heroin use in pregnancy

- Children born to heroin-addicted mothers are at greater risk of SIDS (Sudden Infant Death syndrome).

- Although infants born to mothers taking prescribed methadone may show signs of physical dependence, they can be treated easily and safely in the nursery.

- Research has demonstrated also that the effects of prenatal exposure to methadone are relatively benign.

The Potential Effects of Ecstasy use in pregnancy

- There have been few studies on how Ecstasy may affect pregnancy. One small study did find a possible increase in congenital heart defects and, in females only, of a skeletal defect called clubfoot (both or one foot appears internally rotated at the ankle). Babies exposed to Ecstasy before birth also may face some of the same risks as babies exposed to other types of amphetamines.

The Potential Effects of Amphetamine use in pregnancy

- The long-term outlook for these children is not known. Children who are born with low birth weight are at increased risk of learning and other problems. Children with reduced head circumference (small size of the head) are more likely to have learning problems than those with low birth weight and normal head size.

The Potential Effects of Crystal Meth use in pregnancy

- Another commonly abused amphetamine is methamphetamine, also known as speed, ice, crank and crystal meth. A 2006 study found that babies of women who used this drug were more than three times as likely as unexposed babies to grow poorly before birth. Even when born at term, affected babies tend to be born with low birth weight (less than 5½ pounds) and have a smaller-than-normal head circumference. After delivery, some babies who were exposed to amphetamines before birth appear to undergo withdrawal-like symptoms, including jitteriness, drowsiness and breathing problems.[10]

How Does Prenatal Alcohol Exposure Affect the Human Body?

Your entire body is made of out millions of cells. The first trimester is the most rapid cellular development of the human. Prenatal brain and body development occurs at a rapid pace, so if anything goes wrong during this time due to disease, drugs/alcohol, or poor nutrition, the development of the fetus's brain and body could be significantly affected.

Prenatal alcohol exposure in the second and third trimester also has the potential to cause interruptions to the brain and body development. Alcohol in pregnancy has the ability to interfere with the development of cells therefore, parts of the brain and body may not be able to reach their full potential of development and growth. This is why there are often differences in facial features, body parts, and brain functioning.

Critical Periods for Birth Anomalies in Human Development

We will first discuss the development of the brain specifically and then continue to the entire body. The process development for the brain is the same as with the rest of the body parts.

After conception, cells are created and divide and layer on top of each other. This process repeats itself at a very rapid speed in the first trimester to create the entire brain and body.

The brain cells begin to divide at the tip of the embryo and form a tube. This neural tube then expands slowly to form the brain and the spinal cord. At first, the brain cells start to multiply quickly but the pace slows down during the second trimester.[11]

When the neural tube is formed there are only 125,000 cells but by the time of birth, the total number of nerve cells reaches approximately 100 billion. This means these cells develop at a rate of about 250,000 cells per minute.

By the second trimester, the organ of the brain is "built", and now in the second and third trimester is the most rapid growth of the organ (brain). The brain grows throughout the pregnancy.

Parts of the body are created at different timeframes in the pregnancy. The Central Nervous System can be compromised from the beginning of the pregnancy to post-natal development, or after the baby is born. The Central Nervous System (CNS) contains the majority of the nervous system and consists of the brain and the spinal cord. Together with the nerves outside of the brain and spinal cord (peripheral nervous system), it has a vital role in the control of behaviour and the sensory system.[12]

Your Central Nervous System is responsible for many things: learning abilities, intelligence, coordination, balance, memory, attention span, how quickly you make decisions, and how your body understands sensations to pain, taste, smells just to name a few. Alcohol can interfere with CNS development throughout the pregnancy, which explains why these areas are often affected.

The term *embryo* is used to describe the developing offspring during the first eight weeks following conception.

The term *fetus* is used from about two months of development until birth.[13]

Prenatal defines the period occurring "around the time of birth", specifically from 22 completed weeks (154 days) of gestation (the time when birth weight is normally 500 g) to seven completed days after birth.[14]

Legal regulations in different countries include gestation age beginning from 16 to 22 weeks (five months) before birth.

If alcohol is consumed at approximately the timeframe when a certain body part (or parts) is developing, it may prevent the body part growing to its full potential, be altered, or be damaged in some way. For example, if alcohol was consumed within the timeframe when the upper lip is developing, the lip might not grow to its full potential, or the shape of the lip could be changed from what it may have looked like if alcohol had not been present.

These alterations can occur with any organ, muscle, bone, fingernails, and skin etc., in other words, any fibre of the developing embryo/fetus depending on the timeframe.

Other teratogens (things that can harm an embryo/fetus) such as prescription medications, virus, or other syndromes during certain timeframes in the pregnancy have the potential to *restrict* or *alter* the development of the body and brain as well.

Having several teratogens in the pregnancy can also cause complications including cigarette smoke, or poor nutrition etc. Very often there is a combination of things that could potentially harm a fetus, not only alcohol. There are various factors for investigation into your child's whole body disorder that your diagnostic team will consider in formulating a medical diagnosis. This is why it is so important to make sure your child has a full medical evaluation by physicians that specialize in these types of diagnoses to rule in or rule out other teratogenic possibilities, not only alcohol.

Withdrawal at Birth

Neonatal Abstinence syndrome (NAS) is a group of problems that occur in a newborn who was prenatally exposed to addictive illegal or prescription drugs.[15] This includes alcohol.

- Amphetamines
- Barbiturates
- Cocaine
- Diazepam
- Marijuana
- Opiates (heroin, methadone, codeine)

"These and other drugs (alcohol) pass through the placenta—the organ that connects the baby to its mother in the womb—and reach the baby. The baby becomes addicted along with the mother.

At birth, the baby is still dependent on the drug. Because the baby is no longer getting the drug after birth, symptoms of withdrawal occur." [16]

Typically, Neonatal Abstinence syndrome would be diagnosed at the time of birth, however symptoms can arise after the baby is discharged from hospital. Some studies suggest that symptoms may continue up to six months to one year of age.[17] Therefore, if your baby is presenting with similar concerns, you should seek medical attention as soon as possible.

Indicators of Neonatal Abstinence syndrome.

A baby could present with some or all of these symptoms:

- Jittery
- Stiffness of arms, legs and body
- Feeding difficulties due to sucking/coordination problems
- Restlessness
- Poor weight gain
- Vomiting/diarrhea
- Increased breathing rate

- Tremors (trembling or "shakiness" of the body, legs, arms, sometimes looks like they are "startled")
- Gastrointestinal distress (severely gassy, tummy trouble), projectile vomiting (shoots out)
- Difficulty feeding (the baby is often keen to feed but cannot suck or swallow properly)
- Fever
- Mottling (blotchy skin)
- Sneezing seizures (several sneezes one after the other)
- Stuffy nose
- High pitched cry
- Scratching themselves (tiny mittens are used to prevent abrasions)
- Extreme sensitivities to light, sound, touch, smells, and movement
- Extremely agitated
- Wakefulness (not sleeping for long periods of time)
- Disrupted sleep patterns (sleeping at random, too long or too little, difficulty settling into sleep after feeding)
- Seizures (convulsions require emergency intervention, including calling an ambulance)[18]

In the event the baby presents with some of these symptoms, your physician and/or nurse may suggest a number of treatment strategies that will guide you in strengthening the bond including tightly wrapping the baby in a blanket, skin-to-skin contact, and keeping noise, movement and light levels at a minimum. (Please see Appendix C for further details).

Diagnosis of FASD

Only a medical doctor *trained specifically in Fetal Alcohol Spectrum Disorder diagnostics* is qualified to evaluate and determine a diagnosis. Specifically, a pediatrician or geneticist are qualified. A geneticist is a doctor who specializes in various types of syndromes, DNA mutations, or medical issues that can be passed down in a family through the generations.[19] The physician completes a physical examination and reviews all of the provided information about the child's health, social and developmental histories.

A psychologist or neuropsychologist is not qualified to diagnose FASD as they are not medical doctors. FASD is a *medical* diagnosis, not a mental health diagnosis. It is *critical* for children of adoption to be thoroughly physically examined by a doctor to rule in, or out, other possible medical issues.

Intelligence Quotients testing (I.Q.) also referred to as cognitive, psychological, or psycho-educational testing, is done by the diagnostic team psychologist at approximately the same time as the patient's physical examination. The type of testing may vary from clinic to clinic.

The entire evaluation includes identifying the patient's overall functioning in physical issues (body), cognitive (brain/thinking) abilities, sensory integration (how we "sense" information), as well as take into consideration their social history. The FASD diagnostic team will also investigate whether the biological mother consumed alcohol and/or drugs in her pregnancy (maternal consumption), her health, and social histories.

There are certain behaviours that have been medically documented to occur more frequently in individuals living with developmental disabilities including FASD. Therefore, questions are asked regarding any particular behaviours that the child may have been demonstrating consistently over a period of time. Strengths and abilities of the child are also identified throughout the diagnostic process.

At what age can FASD be diagnosed?

It is very difficult for physicians to diagnose a newborn or an infant due to natural changes in some facial features. For example, the tiny webs of skin (called the epicanthi) covering the inner corner of the eye, naturally disappears over time. A "ski-sloped" nose (called a low nasal bridge) is normal in babies, but not in older children.

Further, an evaluation of age appropriate global development (at what age they reach milestones such as rolling over, standing, walking, talking, toileting, etc.) *over time* is required to determine the possibility of any detrimental effects.

In general, it is recommended that *all* children presenting with developmental delays be medically and cognitively evaluated before they enter grade one or are of six years of age. Intelligence Quotient (I.Q.) also referred to, as cognitive, psychological, or psycho-educational, testing is an assessment of the child's abilities. In cases where FASD is suspected, this testing is completed by the FASD Diagnostic team psychologist.

Patients who are diagnosed as small children typically require a medical review when they get older to determine their progress. The FASD diagnostic physician and team would decide the timeframe of follow-up.

How is FASD diagnosed?

The degree of organic brain injury/dysfunction is determined by a medical FASD team consisting of a physician who completes an extensive physical examination and overall evaluation of the child, a psychologist who completes the I.Q. (also called cognitive, psychological or psycho-educational) and possibly other abilities testing, and a nurse or social worker who gathers information regarding the biological mother's substance use in the pregnancy. Many clinics also have a speech/language pathologist and/or an occupational therapist that would also conduct assessments in their respective area of expertise.

The physician and FASD team typically use a diagnostic guide to diagnose a patient within FASD. One of the most commonly used medical tools is called the Diagnostic Prevention Network (DPN) 4-Digit Code. Dr. Susan Astley revised the University of Washington Diagnostic Prevention Network 4-Digit Code in 2004.[20] It is called the 4-Digit Code because the patient is evaluated in four criteria:

Diagnostic Prevention Network (DPN) Codes 1-4

1) Growth failure: None (1) to Significant (4) =

2) FAS facial features: Absent (1) to Severe (4) =

3) Brain dysfunction: Unlikely (1) to definite (4) =

4) Prenatal history of alcohol: No risk (1), Unknown, Some risk, High Risk (4) =

Explanations of the Criteria

1) Growth failure: None (1) to Significant (4)

The physician and team review all birth and medical records to date, and examine the patient to determine if there was any prenatal and/or postnatal growth failure. In some cases, patients are smaller in stature because alcohol in the pregnancy restricted their growth.

2) FAS facial features: Absent (1) to Severe (4)

The physician examines the patient and notes any physical findings of structural anomalies (differences) of the body and/or typical FAS facial features.

What do the FAS facial features look like?

The doctor measures the eyes from inside corner to inside corner (across the eye).

The doctor measures the inner eye folds (from the eyelid to the bottom of the eye (up and down).

The doctor takes into consideration the racial group and whether the facial features are likely caused by alcohol in the pregnancy, or are possibly hereditary (passed down), from the biological parents. All 3 diagnostic features need to be present for FAS Facial features. The doctor measures the distance between the inner corners of each eye.[21, 22]

The doctor evaluates the red portion of the upper lip and shape of the philtrum (the space and distance between the upper lip and nose).

The Likert Scale is what the doctor uses to evaluate the upper lip, and smoothness of the philtrum by comparing the photographic scale to the patient's lip and philtrum. A rank 4 or 5 indicates a thin lip and/or smooth philtrum on the Lip-Philtrum.[23]

Do all children have these facial features?

No. Some patients have no facial features and/or growth failure but still may have brain injury, physical differences, learning problems and/or sensory integration difficulties.

Why? The facial features are developed in a very short timeframe in the first trimester. Therefore, if the mother was not drinking alcohol during that time, but consumed alcohol later in the pregnancy, the brain (and body) could be compromised without evidence of the classic FAS facial features. Recalling the previous example of a college student that is not aware she is pregnant while drinking alcohol, if the facial features were being developed while she was studying for exams and not drinking, the baby would *not have* the classic facial features, but could have other body, brain, and/or sensory integration problems.

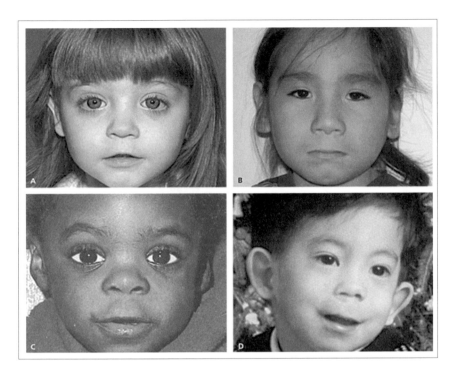

Astley, S. (2004). Copyright 2011.Used with Permission

Many children do not have the classic facial features or any physical abnormalities. In this case, the child/youth or adult looks "normal", but the brain may still be damaged resulting in unexpected, inconsistent, and unpredictable behaviours. This is why FASD is often referred to as the "invisible" disability.

For children, youth and adults fitting this description, it naturally poses difficulties for others to realize that in fact, the child/youth has brain dysfunction. It is *very important* that your entire family, child's teachers, therapist, or anyone living with or working with your child has clear and accurate information. This would include the child's strengths, talents, and abilities, as well as specific challenges, and where they may need assistance.

What about facial features in older children or adults?

In some cases, the facial features of the upper lip and philtrum (under the nose) may decrease over time.

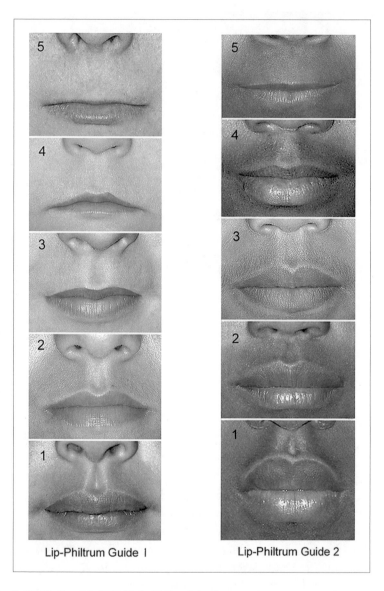

Lip-Philtrum Guide 1   Lip-Philtrum Guide 2

Astley, S. (2004). Copyright 2011.Used with Permission [24]

Some physicians may request photographs of a patient from when they were children. This helps to evaluate whether the upper lip was slightly thinner and the philtrum slightly flatter at that time.

3) Brain dysfunction: Unlikely (1) to definite (4)

The psychologist completes I.Q. or Psycho-Educational testing and possibly other types of testing as well. Various testing methods for FASD diagnosis will be discussed in more detail in Chapter Four. These assessments are intended to investigate the child's learning style, developmental abilities in how they are able to conduct themselves in day-to-day living, and whether their skills are on target for their age. The diagnostic physician and FASD team members then review the reports.

An average to above average I.Q. does not exclude brain dysfunction in patients diagnosed within FASD.

Testing may be conducted on children as young as five years of age, depending on the examiner (Psychologist) and FASD clinic. For children younger than five, a medical and cognitive review would very likely be scheduled, prior to beginning grade one, if possible. Children younger than five would be evaluated on their developmental milestones (when they were able to crawl, sit up, walk, talk, use the toilet), as well by considering the child's day-to-day functioning and behaviours.

You will be asked to provide the FASD clinic team with necessary documentation (as per the FASD Clinic requirements in your area), as well describe your child's abilities, strengths, struggles, and behaviours.

4) Prenatal history of alcohol: No risk (1), Unknown, Some risk, High Risk (4)

The FASD team Social Worker or Nurse Coordinator is responsible for gathering information regarding the biological mother's history of alcohol or other substance use in the pregnancy. Other information such as health, hereditary and social histories, issues, obstetrical care, and prenatal factors are also documented, if possible, for the physician and team's review. In some cases, there may be a major medical finding of brain injury without confirmation of alcohol in pregnancy (where alcohol exposure unknown.)

The various diagnoses and what they mean

Sentinel Physical findings

The term "Sentinel Physical Findings" is used in this diagnostic system when the patient presents with growth deficiency at the Rank 3 or 4 level and/or presents with the FAS (Fetal Alcohol Syndrome) facial phenotype (characteristics) at the Rank 3 or 4 level. The term "sentinel" (means typical) physical findings that are a key diagnostic feature of FAS. These include a unique cluster of minor facial anomalies (shortened eye length and width called short palpebral fissures), thin upper lip, and flatting above the upper lip (called a smooth philtrum) and growth deficiency. Other physical findings (major or minor anomalies) may be detected instead of or in addition to these sentinel findings that may suggest alternate or additional conditions.[25]

Fetal Alcohol Syndrome (FAS)

Growth deficiency.

A unique cluster of minor facial anomalies, such as small eyes, smooth philtrum (the vertical groove above the lips) and a thin upper lip.

Central nervous system damage including structural, neurological, and/or functional impairment.

Prenatal alcohol exposure.

Static Encephalopathy (Alcohol Exposed)

The term "encephalopathy" refers to brain injury. There are many forms of encephalopathy such as being brain injured in a car crash.

The term "static" means, "not going to get worse". In the case of FASD, the brain injury occurred when the brain was developing in the pregnancy. Static brain injury is not going to get worse as opposed to a progressive encephalopathy such as Alzheimer's disease where the brain damage does get worse. We cannot heal or rehabilitate the FASD brain.

This diagnosis refers to individuals who have structural, neurological and/or significant functional abnormalities to their brain (central nervous system).

Atypical FAS

Patients who present with static encephalopathy have most, but not all of the sentinel physical findings of FAS and were alcohol exposed.

Although some children do not present with growth deficiency or characteristic facial features, prenatal alcohol exposure can still cause brain (central nervous system) damage with the same severity as children who have all of the markers of fetal alcohol syndrome.

In the event you are adopting an older child or where the FASD diagnostic clinic has used other diagnostic tools for diagnosis, the terminology may be slightly different.

Example of a Diagnosis and Meaning

Diagnosis: Sentinel physical findings, static encephalopathy, alcohol exposed.

Sentinel physical findings means that the child has confirmed physical features (of the face and/or abnormal growth), static encephalopathy means brain injury, and alcohol exposed means there was confirmation that there was alcohol in the pregnancy.

Neurobehavioural Disorder

The term "Neurobehavioural Disorder" is used in this diagnostic system when the patient presents with brain (cognitive/behavioural) dysfunction at the Rank 2 level and with no evidence of structural, neurological or functional abnormalities.

This diagnosis indicates that the patient's behaviour is typical of children diagnosed with FASD, but they do not have evidence of physical problems, they have normal growth and few if any, facial features of FAS.

Example of a Diagnosis and Meaning

Diagnosis: Neurobehavioural disorder, alcohol exposure unknown.

This means the patient presents with learning problems (cognitive) behaviours found commonly in FASD diagnosed patients (referred to as behavioural dysfunction) at the Rank 2 level and no evidence of structural, neurological or functional abnormalities, however it is not known whether there was alcohol in the pregnancy.

All diagnoses within Fetal Alcohol Spectrum Disorders are considered major medical findings. *There is no such thing as a diagnosis of "mild" FASD.* No two patients are ever exactly the same in presentation physically, intellectually, or emotionally. However, a diagnosis of Neurobehavioural Disorder often comes with similar support requirements or challenges to those diagnosed with Fetal Alcohol Syndrome. Youth and adults that remain undiagnosed, but would meet the criteria for Neurobehavioural Disorder, are at high risk of "falling through the cracks" as they do not "look" like they have brain dysfunction. Once again, early diagnosis gives an advantage of knowing how best to care your child.

Teratogen

Definition: "Anything that adversely affects normal cellular development in the embryo or fetus."[26] Many teratogens are considered when diagnosing FASD as they all factor into *potential* harm to the fetus.

Things that can be harmful to the embryo/fetus:

Cigarette Smoke; Prenatal tobacco has been associated with poor growth of the fetus, low birth weight, and preterm delivery. Patients exposed to smoke before and after birth appear to have higher rates of respiratory problems such as asthma and Sudden Infant Death syndrome (SIDS).

Virus/Infection – For example: Rubella virus (German Measles) can cause Down syndrome. Infections such as HIV, Sexually Transmitted diseases could also be harmful to a pregnancy.

Prescription Medications (that are not recommended for use in pregnancy).

Illegal drugs (cocaine, heroin, methamphetamines, marijuana).

Inadequate nutrition (can cause a decrease in vitamin B12, which decreases the body's ability to absorb proteins).[27]

Various genetic syndromes and DNA mutations. There are at least 50 other syndromes or DNA mutations that look very similar to Fetal Alcohol Spectrum Disorders in overall presentation. This is why it is so important for your child to be evaluated by a specialized medical team, as the health history of the biological parents may be sparse or nonexistent.

Physical injury to the mother and/or fetus. Sadly, there are many women who have been physically abused by a partner when they were pregnant. An assault of this nature often goes unreported, as some women are too frightened or embarrassed to seek help.

Lead, Radiation, x-rays.

Other factors for consideration in pregnancy:

High blood pressure.

Anemia (a concentration of hemoglobin in the blood and can cause a decrease in vitamin B12).

Bulimia, anorexia (may cause poor nutrition to the embryo/fetus).

Overall maternal (mother's) health, previous pregnancies.

Age of the mother at the time of the birth.

Adverse postnatal (after the baby is born) complications. This would include lack of stimulation (being held and nurtured), nutrition, medical neglect, or the umbilical cord wrapped around the baby's neck causing lengthy lack of oxygen resulting in post-natal brain dysfunction.

When a patient's brain injury, body differences and/or sensory issues are caused mainly by alcohol, it is diagnosed within the range of Fetal Alcohol Spectrum Disorder (FASD).

Chapter Two

Identification of Possible Physical and Neurological Issues—Potential Misinterpretations of Behaviours

Now we will be identifying the other parts of the body that could be compromised by prenatal alcohol exposure. Most importantly, we will see how some of the possible physical problems may be *misinterpreted* as the child intentionally being uncooperative or defiant. It is important to note that children with other types of developmental disabilities have the same or similar issues.

Identification of Possible Physical Issues

There are approximately 200 physical issues that have been found to occur within this patient population. Many children will have a small number of physical issues, and some individuals may have many. FASD is considered a whole body disorder.

The **OBD** (**O**rganic **B**rain **D**ysfunction) Triage Physician's Checklist © is a list of physical abnormalities that have been found to exist in this patient population. A reminder, *none* of the following physical issues are *exclusive* to patients with FASD as they occur in children with other forms of developmental disabilities and in the general population of children as well. **One feature alone does not mean that a child has FASD.** The diagnostic physician looks for a cluster or group of physical findings to evaluate to determine an accurate, responsible medical diagnosis.

It is important to review these possibilities to ensure that your child has the appropriate medical care for issues that may require treatment. Also, physical differences cited in this list are often misunderstood by others as defiant or uncooperative behaviour. They will be discussed later in the chapter.

Central Nervous System

- Intrauterine growth restriction (IUGR) or poor growth of the fetus in the womb

- Low birth weight (2500 grams / 5.5 pounds or under)

- Postnatal growth delay

- Small stature

- Delayed physical growth

- Decelerating weight loss over time, not due to nutrition

- Disproportionately low weight to height

- Decreased cranial (head) size at birth

- Microcephaly (small head circumference = 2nd percentile or under)

- Macrocephaly (large head circumference = 98th percentile or over)

- Hydrocephalus (an accumulation of extra fluid within the brain. Often will require a neurosurgical placement of a shunt)

- Subdural hydroma (too much water between the brain and cranium)

- Partial or complete agenesis of the corpus collosum (the connection between the left and right brain is absent)

- Cortical atrophy (part of the brain that is not growing properly)

- Cerebral hypoplasia (small growth of the brain)

- Poor tandem gait (ability to walk in a straight line, balance and position sense, relatively difficult activity)

- Poor hand-eye coordination (example – ability to catch)

- Tremors (an intention tremor is when trying to coordinate, for example, while attempting to grab an object, the hand may slightly tremor (or tremble). A resting tremor is when the hands are flat on a surface and the tremor (shaking) is constant

- Poor endurance for sustained activities will exhaust easily and is often mistaken for laziness or non-compliance

- Hypotonia (floppy muscles)

- Hypertonia (tight muscles, not flexible)

- Ataxia (Problems with balance, clumsy, inability to complete Romberg test-cannot right themselves in three seconds or less. Feet together and show they are able to stand for 10 seconds)

- High tolerance for pain (lack of crying or complaints when sustaining an injury which normally would provoke such a response)

- Low tolerance for pain (excessive crying or complaints when sustaining an injury which normally would not provoke such a response)

- Over sensitivity or under sensitivity to hot/cold sensations

- Over sensitivity to light

- Does not know when to stop eating (does not feel full)

- Disinterested in food (does not feel hungry)

- Over sensitivity to sound

- Over sensitivity to food textures

- Seizures (a convulsion or other clinically detectable event caused by a sudden discharge of electrical activity in the brain)

- Tics or twitches can occur anywhere on the body. Often facial, involuntary muscular movements

- Multiple ear infections (over four per year in infancy is significant)

- Myringotomy tubes required (plastic tubes placed in the eardrum to help eliminate chronic infections)

- Conductive hearing loss (nerve damage that decreases or eliminates hearing)

- Neurosensory hearing loss (sensory / receptive hearing loss, auditory processing disorder—only "hear" one or two words out of a sentence)

- Headaches

- Somatic complaints (complaints about in-apparent illnesses)

Sleep health and patterns

- Difficulty settling into sleep

- Disrupted sleep / awake cycles (Some individuals may require lifelong interventions to help them sleep, environmental accommodations, melatonin, or in some cases, prescribed medication)

- Night terrors

- Restless leg syndrome
- Difficulty waking up in the morning and transitioning from the sleep to wake cycle (their body doesn't "tell them" to wake up)
- Excessively tired in the daytime
- Wandering in the night (may require interventions such as motion detector lights to keep them safe)
- Regularity of sleep and sleep duration
- Sleep disordered breathing

Vision

- Retinal vascular anomalies (or eye disorders that are especially common in pre-term infants. These eye problems represent a serious disability if not managed)
- Refractive problems (myopia or short sightedness)
- Optic atrophy (optic nerve paler and smaller than it should be)
- Strabismus (also referred to as a "lazy" or wandering eye as the eye turns inward or outward.) Identification and possible treatment for strabismus varies as indicated by the eye specialist such as an optometrist or an ophthalmologist
- Your child may require glasses
- Nystagmus (constant involuntary eye movement. Resting and on lateral gaze—when patient looks sideways, eyes flicker back and forth more than one to two times)
- Microphthalmia (globes or eyeballs are too small and typically requires a specialist (ophthalmologist) appointment to determine eye health

Craniofacial (features of the face)

- Short palpebral fissures (narrow eye slits)
- Blepharophimosis (tight eyelids)
- Antimongoloid palpebral fissures (opposite of Down syndrome, which is upward slanting. In some patients diagnosed within FASD, the palpebral fissures are downward slanting and the ears are rotated)

- Ptosis (drooping eyelid—one or both)

- Maxillary (midfacial) hypoplasia (area from eyebrows to upper lip underdeveloped, flattened cheekbones)

- Ocular hypertelorism (wide-spaced distance from iris to iris in the eyes)

- Disorganized eyebrows (a spray or growing upwards)

- Clown eyebrows (arched up like a clown's eyebrows)

- Epicanthal folds (tiny webs of skin covering the inner surface of the eye)

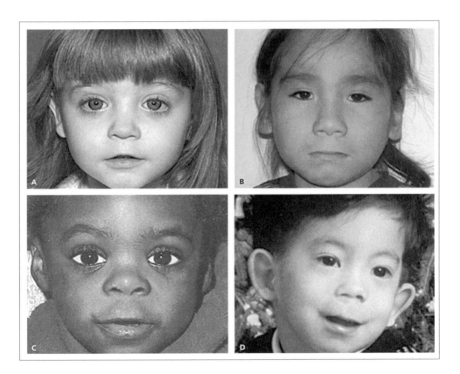

Astley, S. (2004). Copyright 2011. Used with Permission[28]

- Vermilion border (red part of lip border or where you put your lipstick, may have inconsistencies)

- Hypoplasia of the mandible (abnormally small lower jaw area)

- Elongated philtrum (the distance from the end of the nose to the top of the lip)

- Indistinct columnella (widened or flattened, V-shaped, more distinct lower on the lip)

- Short upturned nose (usually accompanied with low nasal bridge)

- Anteverted nostrils (tipped or bent forward)

- Increased growth of nose (prominent in teenagers/adults)

- Underdeveloped philtrum (the median groove on the external surface of the upper lip)

- Thin upper lip—measured on the Likert Scale (1-5)

- Low nasal bridge ("ski slope" shaped which is normal in babies, not in older children)

- Micrognathia (small mandible or jaw, overbite or recessed jaw)

- Prognathia (protruding chin)

- Angular face (long, more linear than curved)

- Small teeth

- Cleft lip/palate (failure of closure of development of the lower face)

- Microstomia (very small mouth)

- Tall raised palate. In the embryonic stages at approximately eight to eleven weeks gestation, the palate, or roof of the mouth is being formed. At approximately this timeframe, the fetus has a tiny little tongue that flutters in and out very rapidly. The tongue's job is to smooth out the roof of the mouth from a horseshoe shape, to a smooth arched roof of the mouth. In the case when the doctor sees the roof of the mouth is very high or tall (raised), it indicates that something (a teratogen) caused the tongue to slow down, causing the roof of the mouth to stay tall or high. As stated previously, tall raised palate and/or cleft palate (no roof of the mouth) can be caused by numerous reasons, not only prenatal alcohol exposure.

- Overcrowding of teeth (too many teeth in the mouth more than 32, or crooked teeth)

- Supernumerary teeth (more than 32)

- Maligned teeth or malformed teeth (dental abnormalities, abnormal placement, size, dental crowding)

- Incomplete enamel formation (yellow coloration)

- Tooth decay

- Dental caries (excessive cavities requiring dental attention less than 4 years of age)

- Dysplastic ears (abnormal position, rotation or formation)

- Large ears

- Low set ears

- Deformed ears (general disfigurement)

- Ears simplistic in structure (lacking in formation)

- Diminished facial creases (smooth face, no features)

Cardiac (Heart)

- Heart murmur (an atypical sound of the heart typically indicating a functional or structural abnormality), arrhythmia (an alteration in rhythm of the heartbeat either in time or force)

- Atrial septic defect (ASD) (upper chamber heart abnormality)

- Ventrical septic defect (VSD) (lower chamber heart abnormality)

- Aberrant great vessels (abnormal great vessels refers to problems of the collective group of primary blood vessels including tube, duct or canal vessels that pass on fluids of the body; are "blue" babies)

- Teratology of Fallot (four separate heart issues, "blue" babies)

Hernia/Genitalia

- Inguinal hernia (groin, associated with undescended testes)

- Hypospadias (urination opening downward)

- Undescended testicle(s)

- Underdeveloped labia

- Hypoplastic labia majora (abnormal development of the two outer folds of the vulva)

- Umbilical hernia (in the navel or bellybutton, more often goes away)

- Single umbilical artery (most umbilical cords have one vein and two arteries)

Skin

- Hemangioma (red and raised, vascular marking)

- Pigmentation spots (low pigmentation or high pigmentary skin spot, uniform in color)

- Strawberry birthmark(s) (skin discoloration (red) between the eyes and the nape of the neck)

- Café au lait spots (distinct, tan coloured discreet spots the size of a fingernail in circular or oval shape)

- Mongolian spots (dark spots, often on the lower back and buttocks)

- Accessory nipple(s) (an additional nipple. Often looks like a mole)

- Eczema (a general term for an itchy red rash that initially sweeps or oozes serum and may become crusted, thickened, or scaly. It may be acute and chronic and can occur anywhere)

- Hirsutism (excess body hair typically facial and back hair)

- Abnormal hair whorls (hair grows in a target fashion on the head)

Skeletal

- Spinal bifida (abnormal development of the spinal structure where the child is born with the spinal cord open to the air)

- Curvature of the spine (abnormal bending of the spine)

- Shortness of neck or limited movement

- Hemivertebrae ("butterfly" shaped, doesn't completely form, more commonly two together)

- Pectus excavtum (chest is concave)

- Pectus carinatum ("pigeon" chested)

- Radioulnar synotosis (fusion of the elbow, limited rotation)

- Rhizomelic shortening (lower arm shortened in length. Can occur in both shoulder to forearm and from hip to knee)

- Klippel—Feil Syndrome—(abnormality of the shoulder blades)

- Flexion contractures (not completely extended, elbows and fingers, cannot hyperextend or have the opposite and be super "bendy", low tone)

- Hip dysplasia (hip clicks—in a newborn makes a "popping sound", dislocations. Double diapering allows for the normal moulding of the hips)

- Sacral dimple (dimple at the base of the buttocks/the sacral region of the spine)

- Limb deformation (abnormalities of the arms or legs)

- Joint problems in general (permanent muscle tightening or shortening of a body part such as a muscle, tendon, or the skin often affecting its shape. Limited motion at joints, typically elbow and the knees)

Extremities

- Clinodactyly (fingers or toes incurved, curved in any direction)

- Brachydactyly (shorter fingers in general, more often the fifth digit, or "pinky" finger)

- Camptodactyly (fingers or toes curved outward)

- Fingers or toes webbed together

- Hypoplastic nails (the finger and/or toenails too small)

- Club foot (child born with in turning of the ankle)

- Flat feet

- Toe walkers (multiple causes)

- Anomalous palmar creases (transverse crease in the hand referred to as simian crease or hockey-stick palmar crease, which is characterized by a distal transverse crease that widens at the end like a hockey-stick and ends between the second and third fingers)

Renal

- Absence of kidney and dysplastic kidney (inappropriate formation of kidney and bladder structures)

- Hypoplastic kidney (too small)

- Duplications of the ureters (a congenital defect of the kidneys where there is extra development of draining tubes from the kidneys. Often discovered due to recurrent kidney infections)

- Hydronephrosis (a unilateral, or single hydronephrosis is swelling of one kidney due to a backup of urine. Bilateral is two kidneys swelling causing recurrent bladder infections)

Other

- Bile duct abnormality, hepatic fibrosis (liver), embryonal tumours, (tumour that occurs during intrauterine (in pregnancy) or early postnatal (after baby is born) development that are usually malignant)

- Pica (An eating disorder manifested by a craving to ingest any material not normally considered as food, including starch, clay, ashes, toys, balloons, crayons, cotton, grass, cigarette butts, soap, twigs, wood, paper, metal, or plaster)

- Cerebral palsy (Neuromuscular disorder determined prenatally or at birth characterized by non-progressive muscle tightness. It may or may not be associated with intellectual deficits)

- Autism Spectrum Disorder (ASD). (A range of characteristics including social and communication difficulties, repetitive behaviours and interests and/or cognitive delays. Some patients have may have a diagnosis of ASD and FASD)

- Asperger's syndrome (a developmental disorder characterized by impaired social and occupational skills, by normal language and cognitive development, and by restricted, repetitive, and stereotyped patterns of behaviour, interests, and activities often with above average performance in a narrow field against a general background of deficient functioning. In some rare cases, Asperger's syndrome has been misdiagnosed when, in fact, the cause of the dysfunction is related to prenatal alcohol misuse)

Physical Issues and Potential Misinterpretation of Behaviour

The following are as described by parents and individuals living with Fetal Alcohol Spectrum Disorder based on their personal experiences.

Low endurance for sustained activity. The child tires very quickly. If left unidentified, children, youth or adults may appear lazy or uncooperative if people are not aware of this physical problem. An example of this is when a child is asked to run with his or her classmates around the gymnasium and runs a quarter of the way and then sits down and "quits" because they are unable to exert their bodies any further. If left unidentified, the teacher may view this behaviour as "lazy" or "uncooperative" when in fact; it is simply part of the child or teen's medical diagnosis.

Chronic illness of the bowels (bathroom issues), kidney issues. The individual may repeatedly need to use the bathroom at school, which could be misinterpreted as avoiding doing their work if teachers are not informed that this is part of their medical diagnosis. Also, poor bathroom hygiene (wiping their bottom) may be as a result of constipation, and not laziness.

A tall raised palate. A child may have great difficulty getting food that is "stuck" in the roof of their mouth dislodged. For others that are not aware of the condition, they may presume that the child is rude by putting something in their mouth to "dig" it out, or that they have poor parenting.

Very short fingers with bending at the joints may may cause difficulty undertaking tasks such as beading, or playing a guitar.

A child or teenager with *hypotonicity*, or "*flabby*" muscles may appear uncooperative when they refuse or do poorly when asked to do tasks that require strength. For example, rope climbing in school.

Your child could be a "*loud*" talker. Some may presume that a child or youth that speaks loudly may be purposely attention seeking, or is ill mannered. Recurrent ear infections in infancy, or as an older child might cause scar tissue rendering the child to not "hear" how loud they are speaking. Alternatively, this may also be caused by a neurological dysfunction.

Lack of eye contact. Although lack of eye contact may be sensory related or cultural, some may presume that a child is being disrespectful if they will not make eye contact.

Problems with fine motor skills (small muscle groups). Adults may assume that the child is a "messy" printer or writer because they are not trying or practicing enough.

Difficulty with a core centre of balance (motor skills). Some children may have great difficulty riding a bike even over repeated attempts. They may quit or become frustrated looking like a "bad sport" not wanting to try again, when in fact their bodies are unstable making it exceedingly difficult to balance themselves in that position.

Toe walkers may be misunderstood as "showing off" or being dramatic.

Joint problems may be misunderstood as a child or youth chronically complaining for attention. In young adults, undiagnosed joint problems may be assumed to be "growing pains", when in fact they are as result of misaligned joints.

A child or youth with a *bilateral ptosis* (drooping of both eyelids) may be perceived by others (teachers or community members for example), as not getting enough sleep or in some cases, that the youth is intoxicated based on the "relaxed" look of the eyelids.

Intention tremors where the hand "trembles" on reach to an object could be misinterpreted as nervousness, anxiety or in the case of youth and adults, as lying.

Small in stature. Unfortunately in our society some individuals will tease boys and men in particular because of their small physique causing an impact to the self-esteem.

Individuals who are *larger in stature* (and not growth restricted) may be seen as more capable than they are, even though they have many challenges requiring supports. Some people may inaccurately assume that the child/youth does not have FASD based on the previous literature stating severe growth restriction.

Mongolian spots. Dark spots, often on the lower back and buttocks. At times mistaken as bruising and leading to mistaken reports of possible child physical abuse.

Pectus carinatum ("pigeon" chested). Unknowledgeable adults or other children may see some girls, as "seeking inappropriate attention", because their chest is protruding outwards. For boys, it may appear to others as them being pretentiousness or "acting tough".

Disorganized eyebrows (a spray or growing upwards.) There have been cases where children and/or youth have pulled out eyebrow hairs, due to the irritation of them being constantly stray, or not fashionable. That behaviour could be misinterpreted as anxiety or a type of "self-harming". Caution must be used in considering all potential reasons for this behaviour. In excessive cases, professional consultation may be required.

Diminished facial creases (smooth face, no smile lines). In the case of the patient who has few or no facial lines, it may appear to others that they are not engaging in therapy, are not interested in a conversation, or have a "lack of affect" due to what appears to be, a lack of facial expression. If this is the case for your child, all professionals and family members should be advised of this condition so that inaccurate assumptions are not made.

Tics or twitches which can occur anywhere on the body. Often they are facial, involuntary muscular movements. Professionals who are not aware of a patient's tics or twitches may incorrectly believe that the child or youth is seeking attention, or nervousness.

Individuals that have an unusually *small mouth* often have great difficulty with large or sharp cutlery fitting into their mouth causing upset or refusal to eat certain foods, such as soup with a large spoon. In some cases, they take much longer to eat their food than others which could been misinterpreted as intentionally taking too much time at the lunch table.

Problems with vision. Combined with frequently loosing things, such as eyeglasses, some children may be viewed as un-cooperative or lazy when, actually, they are unable to see properly. Eyesight problems are very common within the FASD patient population; therefore all family and professionals involved with your child should be made aware of any concerns in this area.

Problems with enuresis or encopresis (wetting and soiling). In the case of an older child adoption or if your child continues to have problems in one or both areas, it is essential to ensure they are seen by a pediatric physician to explore physical possibilities. Unfortunately, there have been cases where a child has been presumed to be intentionally wetting or soiling when in fact it was a physical problem that was never evaluated. For children who have suffered previous physical, sexual and/or emotional abuse, it is *critical* to seek medical assessment *before presuming the behaviour is a result of previous abuse.* This is not to suggest that all children that have experienced abuse are wetting or soiling only due to an undiagnosed medical condition, rather, that exploration of the physical possibilities with the appropriate medical specialist should be done first.

Making a mess in the bathroom. Hypospadias is where the urination opening is downward, which can cause inaccurate aim in the toilet.

Having social boundaries is *feeling* how you act. Some children with FASD have a problem understanding what they are doing is not appropriate since they are not able to sense things.

Standing too close to others might appear physically intrusive when essentially they may not "feel" how close they are to someone else.

Verbally intrusive behaviour such as excessive talking, or talking loudly can be easily misjudged by others as being self-centred or wanting attention. We must consider that they may not realize that they are speaking too much or too loudly. Kind cues are suggested to assist those who have difficulties in this area.

Misinterpreting facial expressions and social expectations. A child may have problems reading other people's faces and/or actions and not respond as others expect them to.

On occasion, families may feel like their child does not love them. Very often, it is a matter of the child or youth not being able to understand, or *show their emotions like other children.*

Trouble sleeping for teenagers (in the long term) if not identified, could be mistaken for being uncooperative, or exerting their need for independence at bedtime, or when they are not able to get up in the morning. All teenagers require a great deal of sleep however, those with chronic sleep problems and living with FASD need to rest when they can and to catch-up if possible.

Motor skills

a) *Fine motor skills* are the use of precise coordinated movements in such activities as writing, buttoning, cutting, tracing, or visual tracking. They involve strength, dexterity and fine motor control. Some children may improve in these areas and some always have difficulty in these areas throughout their life course.

b) *Gross motor skills* are the ability to use large muscle groups that coordinate body movements involved in activities such as walking, running, jumping, throwing, and maintaining balance. They involve muscle tone and strength. As with fine motor skills, some gross motor skills may improve over time however, many individuals have lifelong difficulties.

c) *Balance* is tested by using the Romberg examination. You may be familiar with a version of Romberg testing in some States when police suspect that the driver has been drinking. Individuals are asked to close their eyes and touch their nose with their fingers and walk in a straight line with one foot behind the other. This is often the type of test that the doctor performs in an FASD Diagnostic Clinic examination to be able to evaluate motor abilities.

The technical explanation of Romberg testing: The basis of this test is that balance comes from the combination of several neurological systems, namely proprioception, vestibular input, and vision. If any two of these systems are working the person should be able to demonstrate a fair degree of balance. The key to the test is that vision is taken away by asking the patient to close their eyes. This leaves only two of the three systems remaining and if there is a vestibular disorder (cerebellar dysfunction) or a sensory disorder (proprioceptive dysfunction) the patient will become much more imbalanced.

Most types of balance disorders will require balance training often done with a physiotherapist.

Some individuals will have a *tendency to be clumsy* and have *way more* accidents than other children, youth or adults. To them, things may be closer or farther away than they appear. This can result in the child having *trouble negotiating themselves around people or things*. They may experience *poor physical performance. However many individuals living with FASD and sensory related difficulties are not affected in coordination and balance, are very athletic,* and excel at sports.

Other Neurological Findings that may Translate to Behaviour

May have problems understanding cause and effect situations. Most children will think to themselves, "If I do this (break my brother's toy) then that (I will get a timeout) will happen" For some children this concept is not available to them due to processing problems in their brain.

 A child may not learn from repeated natural, logical, consequences. Children that do not seem to learn from consequences very often *simply do not understand what they did wrong* due to their medical form of brain dysfunction.

 Some children engage in *"collecting other people's things"*, better known as stealing. Why? It is a combination of cognitive problems including memory, being able to understand the concept of ownership, problems with processing abstract concepts. If the owner of an object is not there, they are an abstract concept. Added to this may be the inability to think about the cause and effect (if I take this, I will get into trouble). This is a complicated behaviour; nonetheless many strategies have been developed to reduce the incidence of this regularly occurring. For some children, locking up valuables may be necessary to reduce their opportunity to get into trouble for doing something they truly do not grasp is wrong.

Impulsiveness is the number one most commonly reported behaviour in children with FASD. In short, it means that one does not think before acting. Impulsivity can create difficulties for anyone as we all experience making an impulsive decision. Children, youth and adults living with FASD just do impulsive things more often due to the problems with the brain's wiring. Children that are extremely impulsive may require increased supervision, as they tend to have more accidents by moving too quickly or not being able to think an action through. An example of this would be deciding to quickly turn left on a bike before checking for a car.

Distractibility can appear to be defiant non-compliant behaviours and is common in this patient population. For example, if you ask your child to put their coat on the hook but they get distracted by the dog crossing their path; they might leave the coat on the floor and go play completely forgetting what they were supposed to do. This is not an act of intentional defiance or laziness. Rather, it is a child forgetting the direction because the family dog distracted her. Anticipation and gentle reminders to get things done are our best efforts in giving a child support rather than discipline them for something they basically forgot.

Poor sequencing skills are trouble putting things in logical order. They might get times or events mixed up when asked to describe where they were. Poor abilities in sequencing may *look like* they are not telling the truth when asked where they were at a certain time. The Psychologist who has completed your child's cognitive testing would be the appropriate professional to speak to regarding your child's strengths and weaknesses in learning abilities.

Emotionally reactive

May become easily defensive.

Perseveration behaviours means that they may get "stuck" on things, for example, repeating a request a number of times.

Lack of control and quick escalation when upset, tantrums.

Some children do not have an internal regulatory "switch" so it might be extremely hard for their brain and bodies to 'know' how and when to calm down. This behaviour can be managed by understanding the causes and to be willing to be patient and calm. It helps to appreciate it is something they have no control over. In some instances for some children, we need to accept them as they are.

Sensory Integration/Processing

Sensory Integration (SI)/Processing (SP) is how we filter and feel information.

This would include how over or under sensitive we are. It is about your abilities to filter bright lights, loud sounds, and how things feel on your skin, or how they smell to you, and how aware you are with movement around you.

Additionally, we will identify how some of these sensory problems might be misunderstood by others as the child acting out, or being intentionally oppositional. More often than not, inappropriate actions are rooted in the child's physical and neurological make-up leaving them little to no control over their actions in some areas of functioning.

We all have variations of our senses. As you read through this chapter, ask yourself if you can relate to some of these things. This will give you a better idea of how difficult it might be for your child to cope with extremely amplified or dulled sensory experiences.

An Occupational Therapist (OT) is the medical professional that is qualified to assess your child to determine if they present with any of the following issues. This is often completed at the time of the FASD medical evaluation. If it is not completed at the time of the medical assessment, you could ask your doctor to request an Occupational Therapy evaluation.

The OT will provide you with strategies to assist you in helping your child cope with specific Sensory Integration (SI) issues if they are present. The goal of the occupational therapist is to enable your child to participate in the activities of everyday life. This would include sleeping, feeding, toileting, learning and playing.

How Sensory Integration Disorder (SID) May Appear to be Uncooperative Behaviour

Having a combination of Sensory Integration issues can be very confusing and frustrating to the child, siblings, parents, extended family members, teachers and babysitters. This is why it is so important to have a proper assessment. Carol Stock Kranowitz, author of "The Out-of-Sync-Child" (Revised 2005), explains the following:

> "The child with sensory dysfunction does not necessarily exhibit every characteristic. The child with vestibular dysfunction may have poor balance but good muscle tone.
>
> Sometimes the child will show characteristics of a dysfunction one day but not the next. For instance, the child with proprioceptive problems may trip over every bump in the pavement on Friday yet score every soccer goal on Saturday.

Sometimes the child will show characteristics of a dysfunction but not have that dysfunction. For example, the child who withdraws from being touched may seem to be hypersensitive to tactile stimulation but may, instead, have an emotional problem.

The child may be both hypersensitive (over) and hyposensitive (under). For instance, the child may be extremely sensitive to light touch, jerking away from a soft pat on the shoulder, while being rather indifferent to the deep pain of inoculation."[29]

Remember, "Inconsistency is a hallmark of every neurological dysfunction."[30] The fact that your child may be presenting with some of these issues and sometimes not is frustrating for you, but imagine how frustrating it is for your child. Unpredictability of when or where reactions may occur might lead others to believe that your child is "doing it on purpose" when the behaviour is not seen with regularity. An Occupational Therapist (OT) will be able to assess your child and help you figure out what is sensory related and what is not.

Most importantly, we will learn how these sensory integration differences might lead to *what appears to be* intentionally stubborn or unruly behaviour. In fact, the behaviour is very possibly a direct result of their medical diagnosis within FASD. The good news is that you can help your child to reduce their anxiety by acknowledging their special combination of over or under sensitivities. This can be done by making changes to their environments at home, school, and in the within community.

As stated previously, children and youth may have some, but not all potential Sensory Integration (SI) issues. Some individuals have very normal responses to light, sound, touch, smell, hunger, hot/cold, pain, taste, (stimuli) and some experience very severe reactions.

Persons living with FASD may have no sensory integration difficulties. However, many individuals may be very over sensitive or extremely under sensitive in the following areas:

Tactile (Touch)

High tolerance for pain. An example of this is when your child does not react, as they should when they are injured. It is very important to evaluate their pain threshold over time to ensure your doctor or emergency room triage nurses are advised so they more accurately assess their situation. A high tolerance for pain is a safety issue as they may not feel how hurt or ill they are. School staff, family members, babysitters, or anyone dealing with your child in any way should be alerted to be sure they have appropriate medical attention if needed.

Low tolerance for pain. A low tolerance for pain may be mistaken as the child being "an attention seeker" or a "Drama King or Queen", as they demonstrate behaviour more appropriate for an intense accident. Further, if not identified, it can be very hurtful to a child if their pain is not acknowledged and validated by others, for example, being called a "big baby" when they actually feel real pain causing feelings of unimportance or poor self-worth.

Smell (Olfactory)

The child may *enjoy strong odours* such as perfumes, cleaning fluids, gasoline, aromatherapy, or hand sanitizers. For children who do find strong scents enjoyable, they may need enhanced supervision and redirection to safe scents such as lavender or other non-toxic aromas they find pleasing.

Conversely, the child may experience a very *strong negative reaction to some smells* such as body odour, some foods, or strong perfumes. This is because they are not able to filter the level of smell as we can. Odours of any kind may distract them so they might lose their attention, making it difficult to focus. Everyone living with or working with your child should be alerted to your child's inability to dial down certain smells. In some cases, scent-free homes or classrooms are necessary to reduce the opportunity for a problem. Other people may assume that your child is spoiled, attention seeking, or needlessly protesting if they are not aware that the behaviour is related to their medical disorder.

Oral Sensory – Taste and Smell

May *not be able to sustain certain or several food textures in their mouth*, chili for example, or may not like things touching on their plate to avoid the food getting mixed up.

May find *brushing teeth uncomfortable*. Some children that have great difficulty with things in their mouth are often misunderstood as being uncooperative when told to brush their teeth. Naturally, there are some children who simply don't want to comply for other reasons, like staying up longer at bedtime. Your observations over time will assist the Occupational Therapist in determining whether oral sensitivities are at hand for your child.

The child may *not be able to differentiate tastes*. This could be misinterpreted as a child not enjoying your cooking or having no preference for certain foods. Often it is the texture of the food that they may enjoy as opposed to taste.

They could be *over or under sensitive to certain tastes*, which is easily mistaken for a child being fussy or overindulged. Alternatively when a child seeks out extremely strong flavours, it is possible that they are not able to feel how spicy or hot a food is. This could result in a child 'burning' their mouth. In the extreme, others could assume that you may be inappropriately disciplining the child if they tell other people that you feed them hot sauce all the time. Information sharing and/or enhanced supervision may be required if your child craves such foods or spices.

Filtering movement

Easily over stimulated by movement happening around them. For some children, shopping at busy malls, birthday parties, family reunions are very stressful for them as they are unable to cope with the various movements happening around them. You may not even notice, but when you stop and consider how much movement is actually happening in places like this, it is easy to see how someone without a filter would react. People walking fast and slow, people bumping into you, physical games being played could all become very stressful and promote an upset. Considering ahead of time what might be stressful for your child will help you determine how best to help your child in situations like this. The Occupational Therapist will also be a tremendous source of ideas and prevention strategies.

Difficulty filtering essential stimuli (information) when two things are happening at once. For example, a teacher is talking, and another student is tapping his pencil at the same time completely distracting the child from listening to the teacher. It is important that you and your teachers are aware of strategies to reduce distractions for your child such as sitting in a student carol, or using a big table, or sitting in a part of the room that would have the least amount of distractions. This way, you can avoid misconceptions that your child is deliberately not paying attention in the classroom.

May leave a place or conversation with unregulated or non-intended movement. An example of this would be sitting at the lunch table and getting caught up watching a fly and then getting up to follow its movements. Leaving a conversation in the middle of it is considered rude in our society but for children, youth and adults living with this piece of sensory integration difficulty, it is very frustrating. In many cases especially where individuals have hyperactivity as well, they are not only easily distracted from what they are doing or listening to, their bodies need to move. Many strategies involve giving the child purposeful movement during the day as well as gently reminding the child of where they are supposed to be.

Filtering sound

Auditory defensiveness is when sounds may cause a very startled response, fear, or irritability. This could be a fire truck or a school bell. They may react in the extreme as they are trying to get away from or protect themselves from noises they are unable to dial down or filter. Understanding these reactions in your child will help to soothe them in such situations.

Children, youth or adults with Sensory Integration trouble can be *sensitive to sounds that seem easy to screen out*, such as clocks ticking, the sound of the dryer or dishwasher, or fluorescent light bulbs flickering.

For some children, *a certain person's voice may be difficult to tolerate* especially if they have a high-pitch when speaking. Certain sounds that have a high frequency are commonly difficult for them to endure.

Some children may *misinterpret certain voice tones as someone yelling at them* when in fact, it is a different tone of voice than what they are used to.

May find it *very difficult to focus while multiple sounds are around them.* Like, at the dinner table there is talking, drinking glasses clinking, the sound of cutlery on the plate, maybe the television is on. There are a number of easy to use strategies to help a child "filter" the sound such as allowing them to wear ear plugs at noisy times, asking everyone to be more quiet at the dinner table or classroom. There are many books in this area that can supplement the Occupational Therapists suggestions to it make it easier for your child to live with the sounds of life.

In rare cases, some people *find the human voice grating*, preferring to be alone as much as possible.

Filtering light

Some forms of *light might be intensified* for them. This could include daylight, the light outside a classroom or bedroom window, the sun's glare off of snow, and reflection of the sun on water. Children and youth with sensitivities to various forms of light will often retreat to a dark bedroom or closet seeking relief. In adults, it is common to find them choosing to live in a basement suite, or home with drapes constantly drawn, as they are naturally more comfortable in this setting.

May be misconstrued as not being cooperative when they are supposed to play outside, and the daylight is too bright for them or being seated by a window at school, or on an outing to the beach where water, sun and brightness from the sand can result in crying or not wanting to go. Many parents have found clever ways to help their children by having them wear caps, large brimmed hats, sunglasses, hoodies, and sit under umbrellas in both the sand and water if necessary. Simple additions to your routine can make a day to the beach enjoyable for everyone.

Sensing Hunger

Some children have a healthy sense of appetite. Some with Sensory Integration problems might *never feel full* or on the other hand, *never feel hungry*.

In the case of a child who never "senses" that he is full from eating, it may seem to others that the child is "greedy", rude or neglected. Previous neglect may be a factor contributing to the behaviour but again, it is best to investigate the physical and sensory possibilities first to ensure the right support for your child.

A child that never "feels" or senses that they are hungry may appear to be picky eaters, or spoiled if they do not eat what they are served. In severe cases, the doctor may recommend supplemental drinks or other suggestions to ensure they are receiving the appropriate daily nutrition.

These issues could be misinterpreted as emotional eating disorders. However, monitoring over time would determine whether it is central nervous system dysfunction, a problem related to previous neglect, or an emotionally based eating disorder. Make sure to seek professional assistance to guide you in this area.

Sensitivities to touch (tactile)

Some fabrics, socks, or clothing tags may evoke irritable or even aggressive behaviours in an attempt to get them off as they *feel the irritant much more intensely* than you do. Solutions to this is to purchase cotton items and wash them to soften, remove tags from clothing and be cautious of tight elastic band waists or cuffs. Soft and smooth bed sheets would be comforting to any child, but particularly to the one with sensory sensitivities. There may be varied degrees of sensitivity on different parts of the body.

Sensitivities to hot or cold

May be a major safety concern if an individual *does not feel cold* (and doesn't know to wear a jacket) or on the other hand, they *may not feel how hot* the water is in the faucet.

Other people, both children and adults, may incorrectly assume they are attention seeking or being melodramatic.

Sense of fear

Apparent lack of fear. Children, youth and adults that do not sense fear require enhanced supervision as they may go with a stranger, or climb on top of a roof, or stand too close to a cliff, because they do not internally feel the sense of danger. To repeat, not all children have a lack of fear but for those who do, protection by additional supervision is required to maintain your child's safety.

Children with a lack of fear will likely go with a stranger, as they do not sense that the person means them harm. Please remember, your child will not grow out of Fetal Alcohol Spectrum Disorder or Sensory Integration problems so life-long supports with your family and community would be required to keep them safe as teenagers and adults.

Lack of fear can also be a strength! Some adults that live with FASD are not afraid of heights are gainfully employed in jobs that require you to work at extreme heights (with supports).

Phobias or extreme fears. Some children may have consistent anxieties regarding certain and sometimes-strange things. In cases where it becomes extreme, seeking professional assistance is recommended.

Considerations Regarding Behaviours of Concern

As a rule, *check the medical possibilities first*, consult a professional/specialist in the area of Fetal Alcohol Spectrum Disorder, and discuss ideas with parents who have raised children with FASD. This will help you determine intervention strategies accordingly.

Do not assume that the behaviour the child is exhibiting is intentional or deliberately planned to irritate, frustrate or "get back at you", regardless of the age of the child. It is very likely that one or several of the issues we have discussed are causing the behaviour.

Chapter Three

Learning Abilities

Everyone learns differently. Some of us learn best by: seeing information, (visual learner), or hearing information (auditory learner), or doing the task (tactile learner). Many of us learn in a combination of these styles. Individuals living with Fetal Alcohol Spectrum Disorder are no different. No two have *exactly* the same learning style or abilities.

Abilities

Early literature and websites frequently suggested that children diagnosed with FASD learn best by seeing or visuals, which is not always the case. In general, all of us benefit from visual information but that does not mean it is our personal learning strength. We are all unique.

We cannot generalize learning abilities for any population, regardless of abilities. Nonetheless, there is one commonality amongst individuals living with FASD. *They try harder.* As Kermit the Frog once said, "It isn't easy being green", and trying their best is often not obvious to those around them.

This is why it is so critical for those living or working with the child, youth or adult living with FASD, to explore how difficulties in learning may present themselves as undesirable behaviours. There is a big difference between intentionally defiant, and being unaware.

Behaviour Clues to Learning Difficulty

The following cited behaviours are **not limited to children with FASD.** They can also occur in children, teens and adults with other kinds of medically diagnosed developmental disabilities as well as the general population. In fact, you may relate to having or knowing someone that demonstrates some of these behaviours. We all demonstrate many of the listed behaviours to some extent. Individuals living with FASD merely tend to experience them more often.

It is important to keep in mind that these behaviours are usually a result of their *brain and/or body dysfunction*, and not to purposely push your buttons. Parents of children with other types of developmental disabilities often experience the same behaviours in their children.

- Previous childhood neglect, physical, sexual, emotional abuse, trauma and/or exposed to violence / misuse of substances, poverty.

- Attention Deficit Disorder / Attention Deficit Hyperactivity Disorder.

- Several familial, foster, or group home placements (instability).

- Mental health problems (possibly hereditary).

Next, we will review behaviours that the child might demonstrate and more importantly, the likelihood of *why* it happens. Knowing why is vital to understanding which parenting strategies will work and what won't.

- Reducing the frequency of an unwanted behaviour starts by focusing on the child's strengths, abilities, and interests, while creatively helping them in areas where they tend to struggle.

- Resources for strategy development are provided in Chapter Seven to get you started.

*It is important to note that **not all** children with FASD will have all of these behaviours.*

- *Difficulty making choices.* A child may not be able to make a decision in their head without concrete options given to them. Example: "Do you want pancakes or cereal" opposed to "what do you want for breakfast."

- *Doesn't know where to start a task.* The brain is not able to tell the individual where to start. Knowing where to begin something requires having the framework to make a decision and may require directions from someone else.

- *Problems planning/scheduling daily activities.* The brain has difficulty anticipating what is needed to prepare for later on, or how to get organized.

- *Trouble with putting things in correct sequence.* The brain doesn't recognize the right order of things. Example: Left shoe looks the same as the right shoe, not having a good sense of direction.

- *Easily distracted.* The brain automatically goes toward a sound and/or movement when the child is trying to focus on something else.

- *Constantly loses things.* Memory dysfunction where the brain "misfires" so sometimes they can remember things and at other times cannot. As well, they could get distracted by something else like a toy or the phone ringing and forget what they were supposed to be doing.

    i. All of us have sporadic memory to some extent. Think of a person with Alzheimer's disease where the memory is also sporadic or "in and out", to help guide your path in developing kind responses to forgetfulness.

- *Overreacts.* Sensory overload is when the brain, body and senses are completely overwhelmed. It can look like someone is being intentionally dramatic. It is also possible that the brain is not able to filter or regulate emotions of frustration when faced with intensified ongoing, yet often subtle irritants. The child's brain may not be mentally as mature as their age dictates, causing an upset that would be expected from a much younger child.

- *Shows inappropriate emotion for the situation*, may not be able to process abstract concepts or be able to read other people's emotions on their face. An example of this would be laughing at a tragedy shown on television, but not understanding that the situation was real.

- *Poor personal hygiene.* Sensory sensitivities may cause refusal to brush teeth or hair, and/ or the brain either doesn't remember, or is unable to tell the child to do things in the right order. In some cases, they may not want to attend to their hygiene because they don't know where to start.

- *Absence of sympathy/empathy for others.* In some cases, the child simply does not understand that what they have done is wrong, therefore, may show a lack of empathy when saying they are sorry.

    i. Empathising requires being able to read someone else's emotions and respond accordingly. Displaying sympathy comes from the brain being able to reason, plan, figure out things you can't see (abstraction), and make a judgment based on previous experience to tell you what to do (experiential learning).

    ii. Sympathy and empathy are also feelings so if there is damage to this section of the central nervous system, they could have difficulty relating. In the extreme, this could result in dangerous behaviours regardless of the cause of the brain dysfunction.

- *Difficulty understanding humour.* Humour can be an abstract thought. When the brain is not able to understand abstract concepts, it may appear the child does not have a sense of humour. A second possibility is that the brain may also have difficulty following along so misses the humour in something.

- *Lack of happy or sad emotions (for age).* These are both feelings and problems with sensory integration dysfunction may result in one having difficulty expressing emotions they don't know how to label. Also, abilities in communicating might be compromised by the brain injury, contributing to a child looking as if they have no emotion. Displays of inappropriate emotion for the situation are likely related to a comprehension problem rather than the person being for example, cold hearted.

- *Does not take responsibility for actions.* Taking a moral inventory of what you are responsible for requires the brain to process the concepts of decency, being principled, guilt, and being virtuous or honourable.

  i. All of these concepts are completely abstract (things you cannot see) and developed through your senses. For example, when you feel guilty, or when you feel virtuous or honourable because of your actions when you did the decent thing to do.

  ii. In the case of a child or youth whose brain is not able to process feelings and abstract concepts easily, it may result in behaviours such as grandiosity and blaming others.

- *Lack of remorse.* Basically, if you **do not understand what you have done is wrong, you will not likely give a convincing apology**. This is true for any of us and again, **remorse is a *feeling*** involving your physical senses.

  i. Caution must be used here as what might appear to be on the surface an ethical and or mental health dilemma, is much more likely to be the result of brain and body injury. Please remember, many children **do have** a sense of remorse, but for those who innately do not, we can still consistently and repeatedly teach right and wrong behaviours.

  ii. In some circumstances, individuals living with FASD have committed serious crimes and have demonstrated a complete lack of remorse for their actions. This is not the norm in the FASD population or within general public. Nonetheless, if a child or youth is harming others, it is strongly recommended that you seek professional guidance.

- *Quick escalation of an upset or difficulty controlling anger.* There are many possibilities for why people "fly off the handle" quicker than others. For individuals living with FASD, very often rapid escalation is caused by their body not having an inner "regulation switch" that tells you that you are becoming too upset and need to calm down.

  i. Think of when you are angry with someone else and you might say, "I am so upset I cannot even look at you right now!" and you will instinctively turn and walk away in order to calm yourself down. That is the internal switch working for you. Individuals whose brains do not work this way will not have that "instinct" to turn away and require help in learning how to calm down.

  ii. Rapid escalations can also be caused by a complete overload of too many sounds, lights or distractions that have built up. Physical frustration, exhaustion due to learning problems, and trying to cope can lead to volatile behaviour due to extreme stressors.

  iii. After school is a prime time for an episode as the child is completely physically, cognitively and emotionally aggravated. Strategies such as soothing, calming activities that address their unique sensory make-up can reduce these incidents considerably.

  iv. Certainly, in a case where the child or youth has experienced previous maltreatment, this must be considered alongside with the sensory integration issue in order to develop effective strategies.

- *Avoids school or work.* This is an area where the cognitive testing part of the FASD evaluation is so critical in helping guide parents with respect to their child's learning style. The majority of individuals that have avoided school or work are typically not able to tell someone that they are struggling in a particular area, for example, if they find the teacher talks too fast.

- Young people living with FASD have shared that they have *left jobs* because they were hired to do a job they did well and then were promoted to another job that they didn't know how to do or could not keep up with. Rather than face embarrassment or risk looking incompetent, they never returned to the worksite. Repeated cognitive testing at differing age levels is fundamental to preventing these kinds of problems by ensuring their strengths are the in spotlight and their challenges well supported.

- *Poor sense of self-esteem.* Essentially, all of us at some level have issues with self-esteem. Consider if your body did things you didn't want it to do, some things at school you do very well and some are very difficult, people get mad at you and you don't know why, and you don't feel like you fit in with other kids. All of these issues in combination can render poor self-esteem. Focusing on their strengths and abilities and understanding what makes them tick undoubtedly boosts self-esteem.

- *Extremely active.* Hyperkinetic disorders cause the child to be extremely busy where their bodies keep moving, often without them telling it to. In many cases, this continues through the night where the body continues to move in their sleep.

- *Short attention span.* This is directly related to distractibility. The brain tells the individual's eyes and/or ears to focus on the sound, light, or movement that is distracting to their concentration. It doesn't tell the child to ignore them.

- *Not inhibited.* Some people's brain does tell them to feel embarrassed by their actions. Sensory integration is often the case when children are not shy about what they are saying or doing.

- *Excessive talking.* The brain does not tell the child to stop the action, so they keep going. They do not realize that they are talking too much. Here, they need help with gentle reminders when to stop just as we do with children with other developmental disabilities.

- *Loud talker.* Two things are possible. One is that because ear problems are so common within this diagnosis, the hearing needs to be checked first to ensure the child does not require medical interventions. This includes teenagers and adults. Next, consider sensory integration as a possibility where the brain is not giving them an indication that they are talking too loud.

- *Interrupts.* They may have great difficulty knowing where to start something and knowing when to stop. Again, the brain might not provide them with the signs that they should wait until someone stops talking.

- *Constant arguing.* The brain gets stuck on something and can't get off. Some children with varied learning abilities argue because they don't ever feel in control of anything (physical, cognitive, sensory and emotional.) Others may not have the abilities to see someone else's point or decision.

- *Impatient.* To be patient, we all need to be able to control emotions when something or someone is irritating. It is difficult to be patient when your brain does not tell you to slow down and be calm, especially when you have a lot of trouble *interpreting why* you have to wait or slow down. It also stands to reason that when we are more tired, the more impatient we might become. For many children, being chronically tired for a multitude of reasons should also be considered.

- *Destructive.* Being destructive with toys or other items is often caused by the inability to process or feel how hard you are pushing, banging, or holding something. A second consideration is that value is an abstract concept. If the child has problems understanding abstract concepts, then one cent or one thousand dollars to replace something is the same thing to them.

- *Wetting/Soiling.* Some children and youth may have problems with day and/or night wetting or soiling. All medical possibilities must be explored, as there are a several physical conditions that may be responsible including absence of a kidney, or chronic constipation from bowel problems. If the medical possibilities have been appropriately explored and ruled out by a physician, then consider sensory and hyperactivity issues. The brain alerts you when you need to go to the bathroom. Some children may not feel the need to go and others may wait too long. Even though they may feel the sensation to go to the bathroom, they may not be able to judge the timing accurately.

- *Seeks intense experiences* like climbing way up high. Some individuals with sensory seeking needs will often look for an adrenaline rush because their body and brain is drawn to getting a sensation that they cannot get otherwise. Providing safe activities with this in mind is helpful for those needing that level of intensity.

- *Perseveration.* Might repeatedly ask for something even though you have said "no", or gets stuck on a subject or activity. Perseveration is a behaviour seen in many forms of developmental disabilities. The brain starts skipping like a needle on a record making it very difficult for them to let it go or move forward. A suggestion here is to try diverting their attention to something else.

- *Unusual interactions with pets.* Examples of this is when they give the cat a bath and then want to put it in the dryer to dry and get fluffy or not realizing that they could hurt a pet by holding it too tightly or upside down.

i. Children and youth that intentionally harm animals generally have a social history of physical and/or sexual abuse and require specialized interventions and professional treatment. There is no evidence to suggest that children and youth living with FASD have a higher incidence of deliberately abusing animals than children and youth in the general population.

- *Tells big stories.* Some children with certain processing problems may borrow stories that they heard somewhere because they find it difficult to organize and communicate things that occur in their life. They also might realize quickly that people seem to respond to them better with the stories than without.

- *Lies.* Telling the truth about where you were, what you did, and why you did something all require the ability to generalize, sequence, organize and put events in logical order. In some cases, this could look like the child is intentionally lying when in it is as a result of their difficulties with the information.

  i. Most children make attempts to lie when they know they are in trouble. Some children lie because they have suffered previous trauma. The learning abilities are to be explored first before considering the other issues as the cause of the behaviour.

- *A collector of other people's things* (stealing). Children with several processing problems, in combination, may result in them taking things that are not theirs when that person is not in the direct vicinity. They may not realize that the item belongs to another person due to problems with abstract thinking (the person is not physically close to the object to infer ownership), memory problems (may not remember who it belongs to) and/or impulsivity factors (they see it, want it, and take it, because their brain does not allow them to think things through.) Cause and effect (if I steal, I will get into trouble) is a concept that may not be available to them.

- *Physically self-abusive.* Some children's bodies may seek out extreme physical pressure, which could result in banging or slapping their head. Another possibility is the frustration level due to inconsistencies in their very personal whole body disorder may translate to self-harming. An Occupational Therapist is suggested to assess the child or teenager. The OT can suggest strategies to help them manage their stress in a positive way.

- *Suicidal thoughts/attempts.* Some adult individuals living with FASD have disclosed that they reached a point in their life where they felt suicidal mainly due to being tired of the constant sense of defeat and people being mad at them all the time.

  i. Some individuals have a biological family member that has committed suicide, which places them at an elevated risk for depression and suicidal ideation, which is true for any child.

  ii. FASD Diagnostic Clinics have only recently started evaluating youth and adults so their families, friends, or professionals were unsure how to help. Enhanced support services experienced in both FASD and depression, are essential to decreasing overwhelming situations and feelings and lead to a more optimistic future.

- *Sexualized behaviour.* Sexual imprinting is described as any kind of phase-sensitive (learning occurring at a particular age or a particular life stage) that is rapid and apparently independent of the consequences of behaviour.[31] Children who present with sexualized behaviour have typically experienced some form of previous sexual abuse, or have witnessed sexual activity in pornographic movies or in person.

  i. *All* children experiment with exploring their body parts and are sometimes inquisitive about the opposite sex or comparisons with other children. Children that have experienced previous abuse and/or with developmental disabilities in particular, require information about human sexuality taught at their overall abilities level, not their chronological age. Consistent gentle reminders will assist those when it appears that the concept is difficult to grasp. Suggested readings are found in the Recommended Readings section at the back of the book.

  ii. Children with developmental disabilities such as FASD are exceedingly susceptible to sexual predators and require discussions regarding self-protection and close supervision.

  iii. Nonetheless, **all young children and teenagers that are new to a family require constant supervision *especially* if there are other children in the home.** Precautions are necessary to prevent any potential inappropriate behaviour of any kind.

- *Running away or leaving a classroom without permission.* Children and youth that struggle with learning problems, and/or sensory sensitivities variables may find certain places or situations difficult to cope with. This could cause them to be overwhelmed, and some children may have a "fright and flight" manner of dealing with the anxiety.

    i. Some adults living with FASD have shared that they left a classroom because it was better than feeling "stupid" because of their learning disabilities. By recognising that the child is struggling and investigating these possible stressors, strategies can then be considered to relieve the child's worries.

- *May be gullible.* Children are all trusting to some extent however, the child with developmental disabilities might be very easily fooled or misled. There are many cases where children and teenagers living with FASD have been taken great advantage of by "friends" or strangers. It is very difficult, if not impossible to realize that someone is taking advantage of you if the brain does not register a warning or alert him or her.

    i. Everybody wants a friend and for children and teens with learning trouble *and* are easy to fool, extra precautions would be wise. An example of a strategy would be to perhaps pre-pay for school lunches instead of having the child bring money to school. Reducing the opportunity *before* problems arise is always the best course of action.

- *Could have a poor concept of time.* There are several "wiring" problems that could be responsible for impacting time management. Consider this— the concept of time is abstract and if you do not have a watch, how do you know what time it is? Likely you make an estimate based on what you remember in your long term memory (what usually happens at this time of day), generalize the information (it is light outside), and bring it all forward to the now and make a decision based on the evidence from experiences.

    i. A child, youth or adult with problems understanding these concepts will not be able to formulate time without seeing a digital clock. Some individuals have difficulty with an analogue clock (one with the numbers in a circle).

ii. For those with attention problems where the brain gets completely side-tracked, it makes it difficult to remember without a reminder, what they should be doing and when.

- *Might have a poor concept of money* (into adulthood). Value is an abstract concept as you cannot see, touch or feel the worth of something. Many individuals require lifetime assistance managing their money. Certainly, this is to different extents, depending on the person's abilities in making, saving, spending, money and paying necessary bills etc.

    i. Some children and youth are very motivated by money and might be reluctant to spend it. There are some families that continue to be a trustee for their adult child, some may have a public guardian (as assigned by the Province or State), and some individuals require less assistance in balancing their bank account.

- May have a *little to no fear*. Fear is a feeling. When we stand on the edge of a cliff on a mountain, we all have a range of comfort levels. Some people will stay in the car and others will not be as afraid to go closer. In the case of an individual having a non-existent sense of fear, they would stand right on the edge, not feeling that they could fall. The brain does not tell them 'danger, danger', as it does for us as individuals.

    i. Small children or teenagers may climb very high up a tree, or put themselves in a hazardous situation and not realize the potential danger.

    ii. Individuals of any age living with a definite (established over time) lack of fear must have strong support and supervision regardless of age to keep them protected from predators. All Persons with Developmental Disabilities that are unable to sense that a stranger means them harm will go willingly. It is our job to always keep them safe.

- Might have *difficulty predicting outcome for their behaviour.* There is a combination of factors that contribute to the ability to foretell the future. The brain must have information stored about a previous experience (memory). Then it must figure out if that experience is similar to what is happening now (contrast) and what was the order of events (sequencing). From there, it has to compare the experiences and make a decision based on an abstract concept—the future.

  i. None of us can see or touch the future. This is why certain chil-
     dren, regardless of how many times they have had a consequence
     for eating a cookie without permission, they repeat the behaviour.
     The brain does not remind them of what happened the last time
     in order to not do it again. Here again, kind reminders of "if you
     do this… this will happen" will help them along.

- *Difficult to satisfy.* This behaviour can be very hurtful to family members
  and friends if the root of the behaviour is not identified. Many children
  have been misunderstood at their birthday as being precocious or self-
  centred after they open several presents and utter, "Is that it? Are there
  more?" The brain in this instance does not compute value, or the ability
  to understand that a grandparent may have spent days shopping for what
  they wanted because that is entirely an abstract concept.

  i. The brain does not tell the child to do this intentionally to be
     insensitive to others. For most, the brain is unable to perform
     the operations needed to respond appropriately so a strong focus
     on manners and repetition is helpful in teaching the child what is
     acceptable in society.

- *May require a lot of repetition* to learn a new concept. For some individuals
  they may grasp the concept for a while, and then forget it, and need to
  be taught the concept again. Be prepared and anticipate that the child
  will need more reminding because of the brain's sporadic forgetfulness.

  i. Might be state dependant. Being state dependant means that your
     brain does not remember how to do things even when the kind
     of memorization and the type of recall are similar. For example,
     a child refuses to finish incomplete homework at school because
     their perception is that you only do homework at home, not school.

  ii. It is especially important for this child to have regular, structured
      and consistent routine to make it easier for them to handle. Pre-
      dictability is a gift to them.

- *Difficulty following directions.* The brain may only be able to compute one
  direction at a time. Some children can follow several directions at a time.
  Trying to understand a long sentence with too much information can
  cause the brain to get distracted by still focusing on the third word of the
  sentence. Therefore, they can become confused with the initial direction. It

is best to start with one step at a time, and increase the amount of steps until the child has consistently and accurately accomplished the steps over time.

- *May not learn from consequences.* In short, if your brain is not able to process information correctly in this area, you will repeat the behaviour. Experiential learning is the ability to learn through experience, trial and error, and observation. To understand a consequence, which in itself an abstract concept, the brain's activities must include several abilities. The brain may not hold information too long (memory problems) so it does not connect a previous incident to another. It requires the ability predict the future (cause and effect thinking) and tie all of that information together.

  i. Although having a child who does not learn from consequences probably sounds discouraging, children living with FASD and other developmental disabilities are not predisposed to become criminals.

  ii. As one mother so aptly put it, "Michael's brain does not compute why he shouldn't take things that belong to others, he just knows he is not supposed to. We lessen his opportunities to get into trouble by making sure he is not set up for a potential problem, like leaving him at the mall without supervision or redirect him to do another activity that does not pose as great a risk for him. My other child's condition causes her to be in a wheel chair permanently, so we built her a ramp and expanded the bathroom and doors so it would be easier for her. We do not expect her to make an effort to get up and try to walk. That wouldn't be fair to her. In Michael's case, it is not fair to expect his brain to "get it" when it doesn't. Both of my children need our assistance. It is just a different kind of support for Michael."[32]

- *May not understand social rules or cues.* Have you ever been in a situation where another person is not saying anything but you know that they are mad? How do you know that? Your senses may feel the tension in the air. The look on the person's face requires *interpretation* based on other experiences you have had with people when they are mad so your brain connects the dots. For children and youth with developmental disabilities, the brain does not understand the signals or clues that lead us to determine what action we should take.

- *Could be manipulative.* Developmental disabilities or not, children and teenagers can be manipulative. It is important to review the child's overall developmental abilities when preparing strategies to prevent and intervene with calculating behaviours. Developmentally, children make attempts at manipulation when they are approximately toddlers and beyond. Even though the child is older, their brain may still be at the stage of manipulation.

    i. Feeling out of control is also a common factor in plotting to get your way. Most toddlers receive some sort of a consequence for attempting to manipulate a parent. It is helpful to think about and identify possibilities of where they feel a loss in control. For example, they might be unable to articulate what they want to say, so they manipulate to get it. This is something tangible that parents can work from.

- *Immature for their age.* Infants could be developmentally immature if they are not growing and thriving on target for their age group. Older children and teenagers may be socially immature for their age, making it difficult for them to interact with friends their own age. They may choose to play with children younger than they are. It is very important to recognise whether the child or teen is able to handle more responsibility and if not, to adjust our expectations.

    i. One of the biggest mistakes we can make is to increase independence for a child or youth when they are not ready. Each child is different and needs to be recognized for their abilities and where the continued support are essential to their success and yours.

- *Self-centred.* In our society being self-centred unfortunately seems to have become a growing trend. Individuals living with developmental disabilities can present as quite self-centred if they do not have the innate ability to look outside themselves and understand how someone else feels. Very young children are very self-focused and for some individuals with brain dysfunction, they too require ongoing, repeated and consistent teachings in manners, giving and receiving.

- *May have difficulty maintaining friendships.* Some children have a very difficult time maintaining friendships because of their problems with not picking up social signals. They may present as immature and become very upset easily as they become overwhelmed. Some children cannot handle a birthday party because of the excessive noise, movement, and not being familiar with what happens next.

  i. Some teenagers prefer to socialize occasionally, or with younger children for the same reasons. People that have intense sensory problems usually prefer to be alone because it is more comfortable for them and significantly minimizes their anxiety.

  ii. All relationships are complicated and if the brain does not make the accurate connections, the child is prone to difficulties with friends, and adults in some cases. Everybody has their own style of making and keeping friends and maintaining relationships. Respectful consideration of what makes the child more comfortable, such as having shorter visits with a friend, and practicing good play manners with a parent or older brother or sister are a great start.

Key Things to Remember About These Behaviours

- The behaviours cited here are not limited to children with FASD. They can also occur in children, teens and adults with other kinds of medically diagnosed developmental disabilities as well as in the general population.

- The identified behaviours, are usually as a result of their *brain and/or body dysfunction*, and not intentionally to hurt your feelings or not listen. Parents of children with other types of developmental disabilities often experience the same behaviours in their children.

- Previous childhood neglect, physical, sexual, emotional abuse, trauma and/ or being exposed to violence, misuse of substances, poverty, or Attention Deficit Disorder / Attention Deficit Hyperactivity Disorder can also be contributing components.

- Multiple placements and instability may be a factor in certain behaviours.

- Mental health problems (possibly hereditary) are a consideration with all children who are adopted and with children with other types of developmental disabilities. Individuals living with FASD have a higher risk of experiencing difficulty such as depression.

- These issues, *in combination* with the specifics of the child or youth's medical diagnosis, should be considered when planning successful parenting strategies.

Chapter Four

Brain Functions

In this chapter, we will identify the components of how we learn, remember and use information to make decisions or solve problems. By understanding how our thinking skills determine what we do next, it provides us with a clearer picture of the link between cognitive abilities and behaviour.

Infants

Infants, toddlers and preschool children's abilities are estimated by their developmental milestones. This is the age that they are able to sit up, start walking, talking, and are toilet trained, able to draw within the lines etc. It is not uncommon for children prenatally exposed to alcohol or drugs to be delayed in some of these areas. Some catch up and others may continue to struggle depending on the impact of their whole body disorder. It is wise to check with your family doctor or paediatrician to monitor their progress and identify any areas of concern or that require intervention. This could include a Speech-Language, Occupational, and/or Physical Therapy Assessment and treatment.

Children and Youth

A Psychologist tests children and youth suspected of having FASD at the same time as the medical evaluation to determine the child's abilities in all areas of functioning. FASD clinics vary as to the age of the child to undergo cognitive testing so check with your local clinic.

The following information is a BASIC guide to help you understand what is involved in testing for your child's abilities. It is <u>not</u> intended for parents to attempt to interpret their child's reports. Parents should get professional guidance for that.

The Psychologist that completes your child's assessment is the appropriate person to interpret the results of the testing. Start by asking the Psychologist what your child's strengths are in learning and where they require additional support. This will give you a great start in learning how to teach your child to their strengths in every aspect of life learning, not just homework.

Youth and adults who have a diagnosis have shared that doing homework with a parent was very difficult often resulting in a tantrum, or refusing to do their homework. The common denominator has been that the teacher taught the lesson one-way and their mom or dad did it a different way causing them confusion and frustration. Checking with the teacher to teach your child lessons *exactly* the way he or she does is a good start to avoiding such situations. Some children or teens may have more complicated learning difficulties requiring professional tutoring from an individual or agency that specializes in learning disabilities.

It is helpful to familiarize yourself with the different areas (often referred to as domains) of brain functioning and how dysfunction of certain areas can lead to undesirable behaviours. By identifying the particular area(s) of the brain where the child has dysfunction, you are then able to design prevention strategies specifically to their abilities, strengths, and challenges.

"Thinking" Abilities Include:

Cognition: is one's general level of thinking abilities

Attention: how they can focus without their brain getting distracted by things moving around them or sounds

Achievement: how well they accomplish schoolwork

Memory: how well they can remember things right away, from long ago, or take something that they have stored in their memory from a long time ago and bring it forward to be able to use that information in a new, but similar situation

Language: their ability to learn from language and how they are able to communicate information they know

Social Communication: how they interact with friends (peers) in social situations like birthday parties or on the school grounds at recess

Motor Skills: their ability in printing or writing (fine motor) and/or their abilities in gym class (gross motor)

Sensory Integration: how they filter, feel or sense information

Soft Neurological Signs: problems related to the central nervous system such as difficulty with balance, tremors, coordination

Hard Neurological Signs: problems related to the central nervous system such as microcephaly (head is too small 2nd percentile or under) seizures, or cerebral palsy

Sleep Disruption: difficulty getting to sleep, staying asleep through the night. Many children are chronically tired and require interventions

Adaptive Behaviour: includes the age-appropriate behaviours necessary for people to live independently and to function safely and appropriately in daily life. Adaptive behaviours include real life skills such as grooming, dressing, safety, safe food handling, school rules, ability to work, money management, cleaning, making friends, social skills, and personal responsibility expected of his or her age and social group [33]

The Wechsler Intelligence Scales[34] are considered the standard of cognitive testing. Your intelligence is part of your Central Nervous System. Generally, a score of approximately 100 is considered average, with half of any population falling above and half below such an average individual.

A wide range of Intelligence Quotients (I.Q.) have been documented for individuals living with FASD from 29 (*Severe* range of Intellectually Deficient) to 142 (*Superior*.) [35]

The type of testing the Psychologist conducts may vary from place to place, however all FASD Diagnostic Psychologist's choice of cognitive and/or behavioural testing are intended to assess the areas of potential brain dysfunctions common to children, youth or adults diagnosed within FASD.

I.Q. testing (Wechsler Intelligence Scale for Children – Forth Edition) is completed by a Registered Psychologist. Four areas of skills are explored: Verbal, Perceptual, Working Memory, and Processing Speed.

Full Scale I.Q. (Intelligence Quotient)

The Full Scale I.Q. is a *general* measure of cognitive abilities. For many children diagnosed with Fetal Alcohol Spectrum Disorder, the Full Scale I.Q. is *not* an accurate predictor of abilities due to the complexities of organic brain dysfunction. Therefore, we do not rely on I.Q. scores alone to determine their range of abilities. Further testing is required to determine their overall abilities in learning and in life skills. This is why it is so important to speak directly to the psychologist (examiner) for an accurate interpretation of the results.

Verbal I.Q.

The Verbal Scale I.Q. measures verbal knowledge and the ability to understand verbal information.

In other words, the testing reflects, **very basically**, how the child is able to say what they know, and how they understand what is said to them.

Performance I.Q

The Performance Scale IQ measures the ability to organize and understand visually presented (nonverbal) information.

This is the measure of how the child is, **very basically**, able to do tasks.

Memory

The mental capacity to hold on to and bring forward memories of learned information to apply to the here and now, facts, events, impressions, etc., or of recalling or recognizing previous experiences. There are three types of memory:

1) *Short term*: information stored in the brain and remembered over a brief span of time.

2) *Long term*: information stored in the brain and remembered over a long period of time, often over your entire life.

3) *Working memory*: is memory for intermediate results that must be held during thinking.

Processing

An organized sequence of actions directed to some end result.

To handle a situation by thoroughly organizing, making notes, and following up with the appropriate action.

Processing Speed involves the ability to automatically do relatively easy cognitive (intellectual or "thinking") tasks, or things that they have done many, many times, *especially* when advanced mental ability is required.

Cognition

Cognition is knowledge learned through reasoning, instinct, observation (or perception).

Abilities involved in cognition (or intellect) are perception (or awareness/observation), attention, learning, memory, thought, concept formation (or creating ideas), reading, and problem solving.

A mindful intellectual act (you are aware of what you are doing).

Learning

Knowledge by organized study in any area of doing academic tasks.

The process of obtaining skills or facts.

Changing behaviour through practice, teaching, or experience.

Attention

Concentration of the mind on a single object or thought, with a view to limit distractions.

As discussed earlier, many children and teenagers have problems being able to filter non-essential stimuli in order to pay attention to what they should be paying attention to.

Attention Deficit Disorder

ADD is a permanent pattern of impulsiveness (doing things quickly without thinking it through), a short attention span, and interfering *especially* with academic, work-related, and social skills.

Many patients are diagnosed with a co-occurring disorder of ADD as it is directly related to the central nervous system dysfunction. ADD may be due to hereditary (that the biological mother or father have ADD) or unknown causes as well.

Attention Deficit Hyperactivity Disorder (ADHD)

Is the same as Attention Deficit Disorder, however the child or teen is also hyperactive (energetic, or restless).

Hyperactivity is excessive or abnormally increased muscular function or activity. An example of this would be that they might constantly tap their pencil on the desk without noticing, or not being able to sit down as long as other children of their class. Their body moves without them telling it to.

Self-regulation

Self-regulation is the child or youth's ability to monitor their own behaviour.

Self-regulation is when we have our own ideas about what is appropriate or inappropriate behaviour and then choose actions accordingly. In the case of pencil tapping, they may not realize that the action is bothering or distracting other people.

Some children or youth could have problems controlling or regulating their behaviour. For example, they are not able to calm down as fast as other children or teens when they are upset.

In some severe cases, they cannot stop without intervention such as the child being moved to their room in a calm manner. Here, the child lacks an internal switch which tells them that they are feeling or getting too upset. People with no problem in their self-regulation will automatically walk away to calm down when they feel like they are escalating.

Self-evaluation is where the child evaluates what they have learned by looking at their past behaviour, and then uses that information to figure out what to do the next time.

Self-reinforcement is when the child rewards him/herself for each time they did not repeat the poor behaviour.

In adults, this process can be explained by thinking about what we do when we decide to go on a diet. First we realize that we are overweight. Then we figure out what we are doing that makes us overweight like, night snacking. Our plan is to cut out the night snacks and do something to reward ourselves like buy something or enjoy the feeling of accomplishment. For some children diagnosed with FASD, self-regulation or self-reinforcement may be unavailable to them. Parents would then consider giving positive rewards or reinforcement to help them along the way.

Abstract Concepts

Abstract concepts are things or concepts *you cannot see, touch, taste, hear, smell or feel*. Some, not all, individuals living with FASD have difficulty understanding an idea when you cannot actually see an example. This is called "problems with abstract thinking" that you may have read about.

A noun that is abstract is an aspect, concept, idea, experience, state of being, trait, quality, feeling, or other entity that cannot be experienced with the five senses.

Examples:

Emotions/Feelings:
Hate, anger, peace, pride, love, sympathy

States/Attributes:
Bravery, loyalty, honesty, integrity, compassion, charity, success, courage, deceit, skill, beauty, brilliance, pain, misery

Ideas/Concepts/Ideals:
Beliefs, dreams, justice, truth, faith, liberty, knowledge, thought, information, culture, trust, dedication, hope

Movements/Events:
Progress, education, hospitality, leisure, trouble, friendships, relaxation

Examples of Abstract Language (Directions/Requests):
Why? Wait, Listen, Watch, Get in line, Later, Your responsibility, There will be consequences, Get started, Choose, Ask for help, Clean it up, Do you understand? Pick your room up, Get yourself organized, Do your job.

Concrete Concepts

Concrete concepts are things *you can see, touch, taste, hear, smell or feel.*

Concrete language means existing in reality or in real experience; detectible by the senses and are real.

Examples:

Sandpaper, soda, pine trees, smog, cow, sailboat, rocking chair, pancake, spoon, table, nose ring, hot, walking.

Show me, Can you give me an example? What is easy? What is hard? How does it work for you? Can you draw it? Go to... Lets start here... (Give them a visual demonstration), It's time to go when... (Provide concrete example), Tell me, Come with me, Pick your pants up off the bedroom floor, what does it make you want to do? Use picture language or diagrams ("It's like a..."), Tell me in your words, Pick up these boards and put them in the back of the truck. [36]

Many children with FASD do well initially in early grade school as teachers typically use a three-cue teaching method: show them what to do, tell them what to do, and have them do the task themselves. This gives the students three chances to 'get it' by concrete concepts. By approximately grade five, lessons shift to more abstract concepts, or things you figure out in your head. Children with organic brain dysfunction may start to struggle at this stage as the part of the brain that produces the ability to process abstract thoughts, may be compromised. To be clear, this does not mean that the child cannot learn. It means that they require an evaluation that determines learning style, strengths and weaknesses. Once identified, teachers and parents will be able to assist the child by concentrating on their learning strengths, while assisting them in areas that require support.

In the event the child/youth has difficulty understanding abstract concepts, they will require that parents and teachers use as many concrete words and concepts as possible. Also, it is helpful to give them a visual representation that gives a picture of the thing or concept they cannot see. For example, putting a picture of socks on the front of a sock drawer.

What is Executive Functioning? (EF)

Executive functioning is a collection of brain processes, which are responsible for:

1) *Planning*: getting themselves prepared, organized, anticipating what they need to do.

2) *Cognitive flexibility*: how they are able to adjust for example, to a last minute change of plans.

3) *Abstract thinking*: being able to figure things out in your head without actually seeing them.

4) *Rule acquisition*: understanding that there are rules in school, at home and in the community, initiating appropriate actions—doing the right thing.

5) *Inhibiting inappropriate actions*: not understanding or realizing that what they are doing is inappropriate to others.

6 *Selecting relevant sensory information*: how the brain is able to filter or sift out sound, light, or movement that is around them in order to pay attention to only what the teacher, friend, or parent is saying or doing.

Difficulties with Executive Functioning abilities are typically the *essence* of this medical disorder *regardless* of whether the child or teen has a high or low Full Scale I.Q. (intelligence). This is because of misfiring of brain processes which are responsible for: planning, cognitive flexibility, abstract thinking, rule acquisition, initiating appropriate actions, inhibiting inappropriate actions, and selecting relevant sensory information. In short, the child's abilities in independent daily living.

Children and youth with a diagnosis within FASD will require some level of additional support in some or all of these areas.

Overall Functioning Capacity

The Overall Executive Functioning Chart compares the child's (youth or adult's) abilities at their chronological (actual) age, with developmental age equivalencies or age-specific tasks that most children can do at a certain age range. For example, the child may be 12 years of age, but not understand social skills or relationships that a typical 12 year old would.

In this example, the child understands how to interact with other children (social skills) at a seven-year-old level, even though she is 12 years of age.

It is *very important* to determine these areas and monitor them over time to see where your child has advanced and where they may have reached their potential.

This model is very useful for parents to determine where their child requires extra assistance, or what level of supervision is required.

Overall Executive Functioning Abilities Chart

Example: Actual age of child is 12 years old

Skill			Developmental Age Equivalent	
Expressive language	8			
Comprehension		10		
Money, time concepts		10		
Emotional maturity	7			
Physical maturity			12	
Reading ability		10		
Social skills	7			
Living skills	8			
0	5	10	15	20

Supervision to be adjusted to overall developmental abilities
Adapted from: Research findings of Streissguth, A., Barr, H., Hogan, J., Bookstein, F, Clarren, S.

Example of Executive Functioning (EF) Differences

An example of a problem with Executive Functioning would be: At 15, a teenager is running a bath and forgets about it. Later, he discovers water all over the bathroom. A youth with major executive functioning processing problems might simply close the door and not think to turn the water off or call someone for help. Rather, he waits until his parents get home. His behaviour was not to intentionally flood the bathroom; he simply does not have these abilities to rely on. In this instance, the youth would require more supervision than the average 15 year old.

Some parents of children with EF issues describe this as the child, youth/ adult seeming to have a lack of common sense for their age. This very often requires parents to fine tune or modify their expectations *in certain areas* of their child's abilities. They must fully understand their child's need for daily support to ensure their safety and help them to thrive at their individual pace. Focus on what their strengths are and what they do well, while acknowledging that they have particular challenges that need more assistance than other children or youth might require.

How is Adaptive Behaviour Assessed?

Adaptive Behaviour is described as multidimensional and reflects the child's/ youth's social and personal skills as he or she interacts with his environment.

One of many tests that the Psychologist may choose is, "The Vineland Adaptive Behaviour Scale" (VABS). Psychologists have many assessment tools that can be used to identify areas of strengths and evaluate your child's special needs. The focus of this particular test is the measurement of the adaptive behaviours including the ability to cope with environmental changes, to learn new, everyday skills, and to demonstrate independence.

This type of testing can be done from preschool through adulthood. Adaptive behaviour is a combination of various dimensions, therefore, the test measures five domains (areas): From the Vineland Adaptive Behaviour Scale:

1) The **Communication Domain** (area) evaluates the receptive skills (*Very basically*, how the brain is able to understand information coming in), expressive skills (*Very basically*, how the brain is able to give out information), and written communication skills of the child.

2) The **Daily Living Skills** Domain (area) measures personal behaviour as well as home and community interaction skills.

3) **Socialization Domain** (area) covers play and leisure time, interpersonal relationships, and various coping skills.

4) **Motor Skills Domain** (area) includes measuring gross and fine motor skills, coordination, strength, stamina, and flexibility. This reflects the child's physical development in comparison to children his or her same-age.

5) **Maladaptive Behaviour** (area) is an optional part of the assessment test. It is used when measuring obvious, undesirable behaviours. For children who are younger than six years old, a different version of the Vineland Adaptive Behaviour Scale (VABS) may be used.

Investigating how the brain functions for the benefit of your child might seem intimidating, but well worthwhile for both of you. You may discover new things about the way that *your* brain works, putting yourself in their shoes, and how to make learning fun for everyone!

Chapter Five

Secondary Disabilities

You may have already seen the Secondary Disabilities Study from 1996. Secondary disabilities were coined by the authors of the study as problems experienced among youth and adults with FASD. They were thought to be a result of the interaction between behavioural and mental health problems with adverse environments.[37]

This study is widely used and provided invaluable information regarding risk and protective factors for youth and adults living with FASD, but the findings are from 1996. Much has changed since that original study.

It is important to remember that we are now better able to assess children, youth, and adults because of the advances in research because of longitudinal studies. Further, specialized FASD Diagnostic Teams have since been established in most areas of North America.

Review of the Potential Secondary Disabilities[38]

- Mental Health Problems

- Disruptive School/Vocational Experience

- Trouble with the Law

- Confinement

- Inappropriate Sexual Behaviour

- Alcohol and Drug Problems

Mental Health Problems

Depression is the number one mental health issue above all others. It could present as aggression or anger, or sadness or withdrawn requiring medical interventions.

- The criteria for Conduct Disorder or Oppositional Defiant Disorder (DSM IV) require the individual to *premeditate* the action and *intend* the action in order to be clinically accurate. In some cases, the behaviour looks like these issues, but is not planned nor intended by the child or youth. They may have done something very impulsively, without thinking it through, or seem to be defiant when learning problems are responsible.

Other Possible Co-occurring Disorders:

- Separation/Anxiety Disorder, Posttraumatic Stress Disorder (often due to repeated trauma), Schizophrenia, Borderline Personality Disorder, Substance use disorders, Medical Disorders (such as heart, or seizure disorders).

Confinement

- In some instances, confinement (a place where they are not allowed to leave) may be required for escalating or out-of-control behaviours that pose a risk to hurting themselves or other children, youth or adults.

- A situation of a youth presenting with out-of-control behaviours may require legal confinement. In most cases, medications and other causes of the behaviours will be reviewed, or initiated during their stay at the confinement facility. It is crucial that you make sure that your regular physician is involved in this process in monitoring medications to avoid potential problems that could lead to unusually violent behaviour and that you do not put your family at risk. In these cases, placement outside of the home may be necessary.

Problems with Alcohol and Drugs

1) There is a higher risk of addictions in this patient population for several reasons: due to possibly hereditary disposition, sensory integration irritations, and feelings of inadequacy (particularly as learners) as well as low self-esteem.

2) Higher risk of addictions related to physical, sensory and emotional stressors as well as previous environmental factors such as exposure to inappropriate use of substances.

3) Impulsivity is the main factor in relapse for most people.

4) Be sure that the individual is taught alternative methods of relaxation and/ or natural substitutions that make them feel good such as exercise, aroma-therapies, equine therapy, etc. Teach them how you relax and reduce stress.

5) In the event a youth does present with problems with substance misuse and previous treatment has not been effective, investigate whether the addictions treatment facility is well versed in FASD. This way, they can curtail the program to their learning strengths.

Early diagnosis is the key to preventing the occurrence of secondary disabilities.

So why is there so much fear around children, youth and adults singled out with the emphasis in the literature and websites on negative behaviours and these secondary disabilities?

- First, as with some other forms of medically diagnosed developmental disabilities, the brain is intact, but runs a bit slower than it should. Individuals with FASD have a multitude of parts of the brain that were injured, and some parts of the brain were not injured. This is why so many individuals do so well in some things, and desperately struggle in other area of functioning.

- A review of the Secondary Disabilities list reveals that each issue is by in large, directly related to brain and/or body dysfunctions that may *translate* to what appears to be difficult behaviours. So why then does it seem that *only* children, youth, and adults living with FASD are identified to have such a high risk to experience these problems? We have established that individuals with other types of organic brain dysfunction have extremely similar profiles in whole body disorder.

The differences appear to be that:

- Fetal Alcohol Spectrum Disorders have not been appreciated as a *medical* diagnosis that requires support services often *identical* to those designed for children and youth with other forms of developmental disabilities. For example, respite time, additional funding for therapies, suitable activities, etc.

- It is only recently that we have realized how the **entire body and not just the brain** need to be taken into consideration in order to provide appropriate strategies and supports as before, frequently identical to individuals with other developmental disabilities in nature.

- Our society does not view individuals living with FASD the same way as other individuals that require support because it is not an *observable* brain dysfunction. This is unlike the other medically based diagnoses where the disability is obvious to the general public. By nature, we are more likely to help a person when we can see that they need our help. Individuals living with FASD and their families do not receive the same treatment.

- Genetic problems, DNA mutations, hereditary issues, virus or other teratogenic agents sometimes cause other developmental disabilities diagnoses. FASD is caused by women drinking alcohol in pregnancy. It seems that she, and in many cases, the children she gives birth to, receive a much lower standard of kindness, respect, and support even though the outcomes of the diagnosis is nearly indistinguishable in comparison to other issues related to brain injuries.

- As stated previously, women do not intentionally drink when pregnant and should not be held out for shame and blame. Alcoholism is a medical condition. Uncontrolled hypothyroidism-especially during the first trimester, can lead to cognitive and developmental disabilities in the baby. Would we chastise a woman for being careless or selfish for contracting a virus such as rubella (German measles) in their pregnancy that is known to cause developmental disability in their child? Not likely. Judging a woman for her addiction, race or journey in life is intertwined with a sense of entitlement that also disregards the child born to her.

- Families living with FASD and their supporters have much work to do in the way of ensuring our society provides the same legal Rights and Freedoms, available programs, and funding initiatives that are already solidly established for those with different developmental disabilities.

- Some celebrities have publically adopted children who have FASD, but have not disclosed or are unaware of FASD. This is understandable in order to protect their child or children for privacy reasons. However, it tends to lead the public into believing that adopting a child is glamorous, selfless, and free of problems. The lifestyle awarded to pop idols comes with unlimited resources for nannies, house keepers, specialized tutors, activities, and the best of medical care and treatments that many adopted families do not have available to them.

- There are many celebrities and in the public eye who have bravely let the world know that they struggle with issues like dyslexia, depression, suicide, HIV, and addictions. They have likely done so with the intent to open conversations about these issues, and be positive role models to those who also struggle with the same issue. To date, there has not been one person in the public eye that has publically disclosed that they are living with Fetal Alcohol Spectrum Disorder. The current societal stigma of FASD likely prevent such individuals of showing the world that you can be successful regardless of living with FASD.

- Certainly addictions are ubiquitous in these circles. But again, television shows and other forms of media are not addressing the possible connection between the risk of addictions and FASD and curtailing addiction treatment to meet the needs of this patient population.

- As yet, no one has come forward discussing FASD although it is very likely that some mothers in the lime light have used substances in their pregnancies and have children living with Fetal Alcohol Spectrum Disorder. It is possible that the absence of such disclosures is because they might feel that this information would ruin their career, as opposed to be praised like the others that have bravely come forward with their issues.

- This is **certainly not** to condemn high profile women who may have used substances in their pregnancies, quite to the contrary. It clearly demonstrates how our society continues to reprimand women for falling into the unrelenting struggle with alcohol and drugs use even though these substances are abundant in our culture.

- It was families of children with other medical disabilities that fought for support services for their child such as Occupational / Physiotherapy, Speech and Language Therapies, vision and hearing aids, respite care. Most importantly, they strongly advocated for *inclusion* of their children into the local school systems with educational and behavioural supports. Studies are clear that inclusion of children with disabilities in the school systems have greatly benefited both the student and their classmates.[39] These parents realized the importance and benefits of desegregating their children.

- We now know that inclusion is the best choice based on years of research and observation so why it is segregation of Persons with Disabilities happening again? Well-intentioned creation of North American "FASD" classrooms, group homes, incarceration units only for those that have a diagnosis within FASD has now brought us full circle in the cause for inclusion for Persons with Disabilities including those living with Fetal Alcohol Spectrum Disorder.[40]

- Parents adopting children or youth with FASD, or suspected to have FASD need to know that there is much work to be done in their communities to follow in the footsteps of the parents before them. Excellent advocacy skills are a prerequisite when caring for someone with FASD. The ability to help the world understand that having a diagnosis of FASD should be respected, funded, and supported just the same as any other organic brain injury, *especially* since it is usually not an observable disability.

Chapter Six

Considerations When Adopting

In General

Fetal Alcohol Syndrome has been described in all races, social classes, and countries around the world. This includes Russia, Kazakhstan, China, Korea, Japan, Europe, Thailand, and African countries where many are adopted by families in North America and worldwide.[41,42] Anywhere there is alcohol there is a possibility of Fetal Alcohol Spectrum Disorder.

Prepare in advance if you are considering adopting from another country. Ask or take a close up photograph of the child's face, not smiling. It should be taken straight on. For further information, refer to "The FAS Facial Phenotype Analysis Software", which can be found on the University of Washington Fetal Alcohol Syndrome and Prevention Network web site (http://www.fasdpn.org). The photograph of the child could prove beneficial for evaluation by the diagnostic physician at a later date, or perhaps prior to securing the adoption.

Be careful about reading information that represents children and youth with FASD in a stereotypical, generalized manner. Everyone is an individual, regardless of a diagnosis of FASD. There are many adults living with FASD who lead successful and productive lives with variable support. Only four are represented in this book, but there are certainly many others. Try to find out if there are any individuals and/or parents living with FASD in your local area or online that you can speak with directly about their unique experiences.

Patient-specific support is necessary based on the individual's strengths, abilities, and interests, while acknowledging their challenges, in order to promote the best possible chance of success in the long term.

Your child may very likely need more supervision and supports for their age than other children, teenagers or adults. They may have an enhanced risk of addictions or problems with self-esteem as a direct result of their medical disposition.

Early diagnosis is the key to a bright future for children and families living with FASD.

If your child has not been diagnosed, it is crucial that they be medically evaluated by a FASD medical team *prior* to finalizing your decision to ensure that you have all of the necessary information regarding the potential types of supports that will be necessary to provide your child and family with the best possible chance of success in the long term.

Required support may include medical services, financial, educational, community and therapeutic supports for your child, yourselves and other family members.

Many patients at any age will require many dental appointments and often orthodontics.

Many patients require more eye examinations than other children and possibly surgery.

Many patients require Speech and Language Assessments and therapy, hearing test and referrals to Ear, Nose and Throat (ENT) specialists.

Many patients diagnosed with FASD will require Occupational Therapy and/or Physiotherapy as they may have problems with their fine and/or gross motor abilities.

Many patients will require medical evaluation and possibly medications for Attention Deficit Disorder or Attention Deficit Hyperactivity Disorder, sleep problems, night and/or day wetting. Some may need medications to reduce anxiety or depression.

Adopting a Younger Child

You should be aware of the indicators of possible Neonatal Abstinence Syndrome (NAS), which is the presence of withdrawal at birth. Babies can experience withdrawal symptoms for up to a year in some cases. See Appendix C.

Studies indicate that there is a higher risk of Sudden Infant Death Syndrome (SIDS) for babies that experience withdrawal from alcohol or drugs.[43,44] What we know about SIDS is that the babies overheat, which is a common symptom in infants that are in the stages of withdrawal, therefore, increasing their risk.

NAS can present *potential* difficulty for bonding between the infant and parent(s) due to physical factors of withdrawal. For example they could resist cuddling or soothing as they are so physically irritated, or unable to coo, or focus their eyes on the parent's face. *This does not mean that all babies born with symptoms of withdrawal will not bond with their families.* It means that *without* seeking medical advice in what to do to properly interact with a baby having symptoms, there is a higher risk of bonding difficulties.

Adopting an Older Child

If you are adopting an older child, they may have experienced neglect, emotional, physical and/or sexual abuse that may result in inappropriate behaviours and in some cases, Attachment Disorder or Reactive Attachment Disorder. Attachment Disorders are where a child has difficulty or is unable to bond or form a connection with others. Professional support from a therapist qualified in both Attachment Disorders and Fetal Alcohol Spectrum Disorders is advised.

- In some cases, children may have difficulty attaching to adoptive families for various reasons, such as living in multiple homes, memories of maltreatment, or emotional dysfunction. Like any other adopted child, children with FASD could be diagnosed with Attachment Disorder. However, it should not be made a foregone conclusion.

Chapter Seven

Creative Parenting

The **OBD** Triage Institute provides *patient-specific* Diagnostic Interpretation of Abilities Clinics (DIAC) to help families and their support team develop strategies for all areas of the child, youth or adults life course.

The **OBD** (**O**rganic **B**rain **D**ysfunction) 3 Steps Plan of Action! (Revised – 2011©).

- The OBD 3 Steps Plan is a guide to create *patient-specific* prevention strategies and intervention techniques based on the child's unique **physical, sensory integration** and **cognitive/executive functioning** abilities. Everything you need to use this model is in the previous chapters of this book.

- At the **OBD** Triage Institute, we encourage families to investigate whether there are physical, sensory and learning issues *first* and how they independently or in combination, may translate to difficult behaviours.

- The medical and cognitive evaluations that were completed at the FASD Diagnostic Clinic will contain the information you need to get started. If your child has not yet been assessed, make sure to ask for the all of potential physical, sensory and cognitive/executive functioning issues to be evaluated. You need this information in order for you to be able to create prevention strategies and intervention techniques specifically designed for your child's exclusive profile addressing all areas of functioning.

- After we have explored the medically related possibilities carefully, then we consider whether the child has a history of neglect, physical or sexual abuse or other trauma related events. This is not to imply that your child's past is not part of what might be going on for them, as it certainly could be a factor in behaviours.

- Parents often ask, "How do I know whether my child is acting this way because of FASD or whether they are simply misbehaving". The answer is to monitor the behaviour *over time*. Persistent, chronic repetition of the behaviour regardless of what consequence you use is very likely linked to their medical issues. In this instance, it may require you and your family to simply accept that this is just the way they are built. In some instances we can teach to the behaviour, but we cannot make them "feel" something that their body doesn't have.

- *The **OBD** 3 Steps Plan of Action!* This is a strength-based model so the focus is on teaching to their strengths, abilities, and interests while realizing their limitations, and where they need extra support.

- This method can be used with any kind of behaviour because it acknowledges their *whole body* disorder and not only the brain.

- Everyone parents differently so include your personal style to make it your own. That way, it will feel more comfortable to use.

- Remember, we cannot heal the FASD body and brain so our goal is to *reduce the incidence* of undesirable behaviour and not expect complete elimination.

- As a parent you are in a powerful position to educate others by using this model. Generally, people know very little about the complexities of Fetal Alcohol Spectrum Disorder but are likely to be willing to learn. You may come across, skeptics that don't believe that FASD is the cause of misbehaviour or, that it does not exist at all. In all of these cases, being able to provide detailed information in an easy-to-read format is your most effective tool in influencing how others view your child.

- Step 2 is intended to identify common societal understanding of why certain behaviours occur because someone that you are dealing with might be thinking it. Relating to some of the reasons that are commonly accepted causes of misbehaviour will not only get their attention, it may persuade them to be more open to other explanations.

- Clear clarification including examples of how the child's distinctive make-up *translate* to seemingly wilful, defiant behaviours, is the key to cultivating more positive attitudes towards the child or youth by others.

- Informing extended family members, siblings (if age appropriate), teachers, babysitters, etc. will encourage consistency for the child or youth in the home, school, and within the community.

The OBD 3 Steps Plan of Action!

Step 1) Identify the Behaviour of Concern: **Trouble completing homework.**

Step 2) Possible *Societal Misinterpretations* of the Behaviour: **She's lazy, oppositional, intentionally defiant, stubborn, is irresponsible, or her parents are not concerned about her grades**

Step 3) Identify the possible **Physical, Sensory Integration, and/or Learning/Cognitive/Executive Functioning Issues** that may *translate* to this Behaviour of Concern:

Now, write down your child's possible challenges in the above categories. These are the things that you want to be mindful of when you are trying to understand where the behaviour might be originating.

Example:

Physical

Jessica has been diagnosed with severe **visual deficits,** is **very small** in stature, has **difficulty sleeping**

Sensory Integration

She is very **sensitive to movement/clutter** around her, and **light.** Jessica's Occupational therapist said she also has **problems with copying things from one place to another** (like the blackboard and her paper.)

Learning/Cognitive/Executive Functioning Issues

The psychologist that did Jessica's testing says that she has **problems with memory in both the long and short term, difficulty knowing where to start a task** by herself, and has **problems putting things in the right order** (sequencing.) She also has **difficulty saying what she wants to say** because of her **expressive language** problems.

How to Create Prevention Strategies & Intervention Techniques

1) Write down your **child's strengths and qualities** in their **personality.**

2) Write down what they are currently **interested in,** what **activities, talents, or hobbies do they enjoy?** What are they **really good** at?

3) Write down your child's **abilities in learning.** Do they best **learn by seeing, hearing, doing, or a combination?**

Example:

1) Jessica is **kind, patient, looks out for her brother,** and she likes to **help others.**

2) Jessica **loves horses,** she **loves talking on the phone** and **singing, loves the colour orange** and **things that smell like lavender.**

3) Jessica is a strong **visual** and **tactile learner.** She learns best when she can "**see**" **the process first** and then **tries it.**

Now, from your lists design prevention strategies and intervention techniques based on teaching to the child's **strengths and abilities** while best **supporting** their **challenges** (what they need help with).

Example:

- We will ask the teacher to provide a photocopy of the assignment as opposed to having Jessica try to copy it, since she really struggles in that area because of her visual and sensory problems. At home, we will print out requests for her to follow.

- I noticed when I was volunteering at the school that she was sitting behind a fellow who was easily twice her size. She seemed to be struggling to see the blackboard but never said a word. We talked about it at home and she wants me to go with her to ask the teacher for a different seat, so we'll do that tomorrow.

- By the time Jessica comes home from school, she is completely wiped out and having to do homework right away is not working. We are going to try encouraging her to have some "Special Jessica" time by having her choose an aroma therapy scented bubble bath she enjoys and play her favourite songs while she is bathing. I installed a dimmer switch so she can turn the lights down low and really relax for an hour. If she is still too exhausted after dinner, we will talk to the teacher about adjusting her homework to be done on another day when she has the energy. We are also looking into a professional tutor who specializes in children with learning disabilities.

- Make sure to give Jessica a visual/verbal cue so she knows where to start. She chose an orange highlighter pen, and we help her to highlight the part that is important to get done first, second and so on.

- Consider the possibility that we put the request or directions in abstract terms that she did not understand "**show me** the homework page" as opposed to "**what's** your homework today?"

- Jessica is really into horses, so we will use horses when helping her with math concepts by showing her pictures of six horses (which we photocopied and she cut out) and multiply them by two, having her figure out the answer. She has to write a story, so she is writing one about a pony. She likes horse stickers, and we will use them for rewards for completing her homework.

- She has a test on Friday, so we are practicing remembering the words she needs to know from her homework by putting it in her favourite song and rhyming so she has a better chance of remembering them.

- Jessica is very tactile and likes the feel of sand. To help her with abstract concepts, visualization and memory, we could play a game where we fill a big bowl with sand and bury objects in it, then have her guess what it is. The prize—a horse charm! Then we try it with her homework for subjects that are abstract like putting toy soldier in when she is learning things about history.

- We are going to take photographs of her doing her homework and what her workspace *should* look like uncluttered and with her reading and using her highlighting pen. We will then have her choose which pictures she likes the best, and have her put them up where she thinks she'll remember to look at them. I am taking shots of her father doing dishes as well—there's always hope.

- We are getting her to try calling herself at home on her cell phone to remind her of things she needs to do. She can check the messages when it is time for her to do her homework.

- Jessica likes to help her younger brother, so on Saturday we are going to have her teach him his colours by using visuals, verbal instruction, and tactile objects to reinforce learning. The plan is she will teach him orange by wearing orange, paint with orange, use orange paper, point out orange objects in the room, have an orange as a snack, and point out that dad's favourite football team is dressed in orange. It boosts her self-esteem because she is teaching someone else instead of people always teaching her.

See, the **OBD** *3 Steps Plan of Action!* is easy and fun to use! You will find many more ideas for parenting in "Finding Perspective...Raising Successful Children Affected by Fetal Alcohol Spectrum Disorders", (Lawryk, L. 2005). Also, see the recommended readings for more books offering parenting strategies from the real experts, parents living with FASD.

Chapter Eight

Insight from Parents

FASD and Adoption

By Tracy Breher

We didn't set out to adopt a child with special needs. We didn't set out to undertake a journey of learning, frustration, and at times, absolute joy. We didn't set out to challenge every idea we had about parenting or to open our minds to an entire wonderful world of determined, dedicated children with the most amazing fighting spirits. In hindsight, would we change anything? Absolutely not.

My husband and I started the adoption process early in our marriage. We optimistically signed the papers showing our acceptance of a healthy newborn baby and went home to wait… and wait… and wait. During that time we became experts on international adoption options, and endured stages of grieving and optimism. I recall a time when I glared at everyone that I saw in public with small children. We went through the steps of a private home-study and experienced heartbreak when plans for a private adoption fell apart after the baby was born. It took a little more than eight years before the letter and phone call came that started us on the home-study process with the Ministry of Social Services.

During the home-study, there are seemingly endless questions regarding the children you are interested in/willing to parent. We were surprised to find how broad our range of acceptance was when we started to seriously consider these questions. My brother is a paraplegic; one of his best friends is legally blind. They both are wonderful people that have made significant contributions, lead fulfilling lives and have taught us so many things. They both have been able to make those contributions because of the environment and opportunities they had when they were growing up.

We added wheelchair and vision impaired to our range of acceptance. When we thought about the positive outcomes when children are provided a nurturing environment and the tools to succeed, our list of acceptance grew and grew. I have since learned that the broader your range of acceptance, the greater the likelihood of getting matched with a child. But you need to be realistic about what will work with your family and your lifestyle. Advance research is required to ensure that you are informed about the challenges you are considering.

We received the phone call about our oldest son two weeks after our home-study was approved. Three weeks later he was 'home'. I will never forget what it felt like to meet him for the first time. Our second adoption was completed this past summer. It also occurred fairly quickly after our home-study was approved.

Both our sons have FASD and a range of secondary disabilities that are often associated with it. They have speech delays, sensory challenges, delays in processing information, and behavioural and memory challenges. And they are each absolutely remarkable in their own ways. Our oldest son was 18 months old when he joined our family. He is learning how to swim and skate, he enjoys building with Lego, likes to take things apart to see how they work and has a very admirable collection of Hot Wheels cars. Our younger son was 3½ when he entered our lives. He has a great sense of humour, enjoys gymnastics, builds amazing things out of play dough, and is too, determinedly growing his Hot Wheels collection.

Our sons have been impacted by factors beyond their control and beyond our control. Their prenatal history and the journey that led them to our family have shaped them in ways that require long-term, ongoing work. But those experiences have also given them admirable determination and strength of character. They both fight so hard to learn new things, and they are both doing things that they wouldn't be able to do if they didn't have such spirit. By providing them a safe environment for their personalities to develop, their skills to evolve, and for them to success, our boys are thriving. They teach us new things every day. They challenge us, they frustrate us, they reward us and they thrill us. There are no words to define the feeling when they say "I love you Mom."

Our life is very different than what I envisioned it to be when we were first married. We have made all sorts of adaptations in our home to accommodate our sons' needs. We spend a lot of time going to appointments and advocating for services. But most importantly, we appreciate and celebrate so many things that other people often take for granted—small successes like spelling test scores or being able to sit in a desk at school, big successes like learning how to ride a bike or functioning in a regular school classroom. I am grateful to our children for teaching us to appreciate life, for making us slow down, and for allowing us to discover, every single day, miracles for which to be grateful.

We have good days and bad days. And the bad days are really bad. These days make you question your decision to adopt. At times, you want to pull your hair out in frustration. At the end of those days, we both try to find at least one good thing moment. Appreciating the good will enable you to move on to the next day.

It is not an easy journey to parent children with FASD. It is often isolating. In many instances, your neighbours, co-workers, and/or family won't understand what is going on with your children. People in public are often judgmental regarding your child's behaviour. And, there are limited programs available to help our children. You will learn how to fight and advocate for your child in ways that you never imagined. The lack of programs and support available is frustrating. Your child will test every parenting skill you ever thought you had.

The decision to adopt a child with FASD is yours alone. No one can make that choice for you. There are so many wonderful children waiting for their forever family. Children that have amazing skills and endless love. But those children deserve families which are knowledgeable about the journey they are about to undertake and that are able to accept and deal with the uncertainties of the future.

Is there any way to prepare to totally prepare for parenting a child with FASD? Likely not. Research is critical before you finalize your adoption range of acceptance. Talk to other parents (the FASD Support Network can connect you to parents to talk to), read about the range of possible disabilities with which you may be dealing (it is much more than limited memory recollection), and as honestly as possible, have those conversations about what your family can realistically handle.

There is a barrage of negative stories about the challenges of parenting children with FASD. They can be scary and intimidating. While they are some people's reality, I try very hard not to let the negative stories affect me. No one know what the future holds for my family, however my sons have received intense early intervention that we are very confident will significantly improve their opportunities as they grow older.

I promised that if we were ever lucky enough to adopt one child, I would never ask for anything again. But once our oldest son reached a point where we were fairly independent and quite successful, we started talking about another child. And now that we have two, late at night when the house is quiet and everything is calm, we have started talking about just one more...

A Journey Understood

By Mary Jane and Ed Claussen

In the spring of 2006, Ed and I were looking to 'grow' our family once more through adoption. Previously, we had twice adopted though a private agency and were now interested in adopting a 'toddler' available through Social Services.

As teachers, my husband and I were aware of FASD from a classroom perspective and understood the complexities of educating a student with this diagnosis; however, we had no parenting experience in this area. Unbeknownst to us, we were soon to embark on the journey of our life when our youngest son, Max, joined our family. At this time, our learning curve about FASD became personal, dramatic, and highly emotional.

In our initial meetings with Social Services, Max was presented as a healthy, but severely neglected, 3½ year old boy with 'developmental delays of an unknown nature'. We were assured that Max's birth was healthy, that he had high Apgar scores, and while life in his birth home was extremely chaotic for Max, there was never any mention made of alcohol related exposure at any point during the information sharing session. We were told that Max wore diapers, conversed in two or three word sentences, was very tiny in stature and had a very subdued personality but he also had the bluest eyes and the most cherubic face one could imagine. The minute Ed and I met Max in person, we fell in love with him and knew he was 'the one'. Social Services assured us that with a little love, consistent parenting and attention, Max would progress well.

Within a relatively short time of Max joining our family, Ed and I realized that Max had some peculiar social and medical behaviours that began to raise concern that there was more to Max's past history than simply neglect and chaos. Ed and I decided to arm ourselves with information and sought to understand what the root issue might be for the unusual behaviours that we were observing in Max. We then compiled a list of observed and very specific social, emotional and medical behaviours, which pointed towards Max's need to be assessed by a FASD specialist. Ed and I then strongly advocated for Max to be evaluated prior to our signing the final adoption papers as we felt we needed to know for certain what we were dealing with. The information we would receive from qualified medical professionals, we believed would help us to successfully parent Max, and might possibly prevent a family or adoption break-down in the future.

During the wait for the FASD assessment to be completed, Ed and I continued to read books, research on the Internet and to learn as much about FASD as possible. We also told Social Services that we would sign the final adoption papers once the evaluation was complete and information sharing had occurred. Nine months later, Max was diagnosed as having Neurobehavioural Disorder (within FASD).

The past five years since Max joined our family would best be described as a journey filled with many hills and valleys. As parents of a very special child, we would like to offer several points for prospective parents to consider when adopting a child with a FASD diagnosis or suspected FASD.

Get Informed: Learn as much as you can about FASD from books, on-line websites, and professionals. Knowledge allows parents and caregivers the ability to make good decisions.

Listen to Others who have Contact with your Child: As parents, we often have pre-conceived ideas and a certain amount of bias. By listening to others, it is possible to discover the reality of what you, as potential parents, might be dealing with. Foster parents, teachers, doctors and health care professionals have a different perspective that is valuable.

Take Your Time in Making the Decision to Adopt and Sign Final Papers: The decision to adopt is a life-long choice that affects everyone close to you and your family. As a potential parent, you will need to carefully consider the ramifications of raising a child with exceptional needs. This decision affects not only the child coming into the family, but any siblings that are already present in the family unit and the marriage relationship. In order for the adoption to be successful, you will need a strong family foundation with the ability to be flexible when needed as well as forgiveness when difficulties arise. Do not rush to sign adoption papers but take your time and make a balanced decision.

Get Personal Support: Build a network of people into your life who can empathize with special needs or who have personal experience in raising a child with FASD. One of the best supports that Ed and I have is from a family that has successfully raised a daughter to adulthood with special needs. Together, we have laughed, cried and grown as human beings entrusted with unique circumstances. Other important supports have come from our faith, persons within our Christian community, as well as a special friend who just listens (no advice or judgement) when the day has been difficult. These people help us to be better parents. Thank you to them all.

Get Professional Support: Locate professionals who understand and specialize in FASD and support families living with this reality. Ed and I have had amazing support from a variety of professionals including Pediatricians, Medical Social Worker, Teachers, Psychologist, and staff at programs that are well versed in FASD.

Be Prepared to Advocate for your FASD Child: As parents, you must be willing to continually advocate for your child and to look for opportunities to teach others about FASD. Ed and I play an active role in the school system, within the supports of social services, the medical system, our community, family, church and even as coaches on the soccer field.

Consider Birth-Order when Adopting: One of the best pieces of advice in regards to adoption we received from a social worker at the beginning of our initial adoption experience was to preserve the birth order within the family. That is, when the opportunity arises to adopt a new child into the family, make sure that child will be the youngest. In adding children to the youngest end of the family, the rights and privileges of older siblings are kept intact and they are now in a natural position of support and caring for their new, younger sibling.

Remember to Honour the other Significant Family Relationships beyond the FASD Child: To us, this means that Ed and I need to be intentional about spending time alone as a couple whether it is out for dinner or a walk around the neighbourhood. We have made a commitment to this goal in the past year and it has affected our marriage in a very positive way. As well, remember to give special alone time with the other siblings in the family. Hyper-focussing on a child with an extraordinary need can leave a void in the lives of the other children. Make sure to reassure these children and love them too!

Acceptance of your FASD Child: While it is true that each decision we make alters our life path, it is important to acknowledge the larger truth that raising a child with FASD will significantly alter your life forever. There will be adversity — but we have come to realize that tough situations are not necessarily bad or wrong. Raising Max has taught us some valuable truths about ourselves. We have been humbled as we admit our need for support and help. We have learned a great deal about our character (who we are when no one is looking), had our inadequacies revealed and have learned the need to work together as a family in order to make it through each day successfully.

Final Thoughts

In closing, we wish you the very best in your adoption experience and maybe one day, our paths as parents of an extraordinary child will cross. In the meantime, I am often reminded of the words my oldest son (then 11 years of age) spoke to me after a particularly hard day of parenting Max: "Mom, it isn't up to you to raise Max by yourself—we are all going to work together as team to help Max succeed." We are not a perfect family and we know we are far from it, but we are committed to each other in this journey of life.

The Kulp Treasury

By Jodee Kulp

As parents we pledge to:

- Strive to keep our young people safe.

- Focus on positives rather than negatives.

- Respect individuality in each person.

- All freedoms as responsibility, judgment, new skills as talents develop.

- Show we value each person's work and provide opportunity for learning.

- Not criticize or squelch a person's enthusiasm though we may need to redirect it.

- Help each other deal with failure and bounce back without being devastated.

- Talk about person's strengths and figure out ways to maximize them.

- Provide support systems.

- Provide logical consequences.

- Keep ourselves healthy so we can be better parents.

- Accept that FASD is going to change our life in ways we cannot control.

We make the commitment to each youth in our care that if they find themselves in trouble, they can call us and we will come and get them… no questions asked. *We discovered long ago that they are so glad to see us; we usually get the details before we get home.*

We determine family signals that keep everyone safe and respectful. *For some of our kids these have been very overt, and for others very subtle.*

The table is safe for any discussion. If you bring an issue to the table before we catch you it will be discussed amicably. *This has always promoted honesty and openness in our family.*

We strive to find the "right" balance of freedom and discipline for each family member. *Each child is on a different time line for being able to do things, and each child requires different discipline.*

Tips:

- Discover your child's personality, learning and processing preferences.

- Don't discount the impossible. Children can surprise us. Things that irritate you now may lead to a future success for your child.

- Provide exposures and experiences. Coach and mentor them through life's challenges.

- Teach them slowly. Teach them patiently. Teach them again and again. Do not sacrifice the quality of your teaching to encourage quantity.[47]

Happy Tidings from Ste. Anne, Manitoba, Canada.

By Sharon Joyal

Hi my name is Sharon Joyal and we have adopted two girls. My husband, Ray & I are foster parents as well as adopted parents. We live in Ste. Anne Manitoba, which is just outside of Winnipeg. I am 64 and Ray is 72. Ray has four home grown children and I have three. We have our two adopted girls as well as 4 foster children. So we have a very full house—our home grown are married and gone but we have 6 children under 18 in our home. Our oldest Victoria is 17. We adopted her when she was five—we had her as a foster child from the age of three. Vickie was diagnosed with FASD at the age of 4. We were told that she would not get past grade 5 and that we should plan to keep her in Kindergarten for two years as she would be behind the other kids in her class. Vickie is now going into grade 12, she does struggle with some of the work especially math but with hard work she has grades in the 70-80. She has her set of friends and has, for the first time, a job for the summer. Her job is at the beach at a hamburger stand and the couple who employ her have told me that she is really a great worker. Vickie may never live on her own without support but our family is ready to help her in any way and we are all confident that she will continue to have a great life.

Our second girl is Natasha. We adopted her at age five, Tazz is 13 and a social butterfly. Tazz was diagnosed at the age of three with FASD, and she also had an attachment disorder. For years we slept with a comforter by our bed never knowing when Tazz would be found sleeping by our bed rolled up in the comforter. Tazz is very athletic—she plays ringette and plays on an AA team which is the top league in ringette. Tazz also spent three summers playing football (on a boys team) she is a very fast runner and so was the one who ran with the ball. Because we felt this had come to the point where it was dangerous for her as she is the same size as when she was 8 and the boys keep getting bigger we asked her to stop this sport. Tazz is going into grade 9 and this is the year she has to change schools, so her school has a graduation and she was the Valedictorian.

We have as a family worked hard to help these girls without using FASD as an excuse for not doing well. By this we mean that it is important for the girls to feel good about what they accomplish and not use FASD as a reason not to try. Both girls see and know their birth families as we also feel this is important to all children. We carry on with hope and faith, one day at a time.

Behaviours as Strengths

Since 1998, parents who have participated in the **OBD** Triage Institute's premedical screening and/or post diagnostic clinics have been asked to list their child's or adult-child's positive aspects and attributes. The following are a compilation of common strengths.

Friendly

Helpful

Creative

Energetic

Empathetic

Courageous

Determined

Gentle

Adventurous

Loving

Generous

Athletic

Dedicated

Perceptive

Kind

Resilient

Polite

Inquisitive

Affectionate

Loyal

Artistic

Hard working

Is chivalrous

Very honest
Loves to read
Is spontaneous
Wonderful Story Teller
Loves the outdoors
Loves sports
Loves animals
Unwavering courage
Tries really hard
Is passionate
Always eager
Is very honest
Loves to build things
Wonderful work ethic
Is a born decorator
Terrific enthusiasm
Wants to help others
Is very neat and tidy
A dedicated organizer
A master of detail
Likes to look his best
Very close to family
Very protective of loved ones
Wants to please others
Willing to try anything
Good with younger children

Is trusting
Works well with adults
Sees the world at its best
Writes beautiful poems
Forgives easily
Is able to be daring
Has a good heart
Is a great hugger
Speaks with candour
Can build anything with Lego
Fantastic wit and sense of humour
Maintains dignity in the face of adversity
Writes and sings beautiful songs
Is an amazing public speaker
Knows directions better than me
Inspires me to be a better person
Is anti-drugs and alcohol
Has amazing inner strength
Has an incredible sense of wonder
Not athletic but loves it anyway
He makes me laugh
The most romantic man I have ever known
Has a strong sense of fairness
Encourages me to be a kid again
Has big dreams
Is a True Survivor

Chapter Nine

Inspiration from Adults Living with FASD

The following are personal success stories of adults living with FASD. These stories are unedited and in the writer's own words.

Realities and Possibilities

By Mr. Myles Himmelreich

January 30 1981 this was the day that changed my life. I was two and a half years old. Just a curious little boy holding my social workers finger in one hand and my teddy bear in the other hand. As I walked up those cement steps I wasn't sure about the house I was about to walk into or the people I was about to meet. Little did I know that house would become my home and those people would become my family. At that point in my life I had already been through many foster homes that it really started to affect me. It was hard to know how long I would be in one place one day, one week, one month, I didn't know. I would return to my mother for a short time and then back to foster care. Due to that constant change I started to have abandonment issues, how could I believe anyone would be there for more than one day, one week or one day. As I walked up those stairs there was Christine waiting to meet me. Her husband Brian was at work and had no idea that there would be another child to feed, clothe and love when he got home. Brian and Christine Himmelreich had three children two biological, Larissa and Keri and Kathleen who was adopted. They had been fostering for years. After been in the home for a couple of years I started to feel part of the family. Finally on June 20 1984 it became official. I was legally adopted by the Himmelreichs. Over the next four years I started to understand what it was like to be part of a family. I learned about the teamwork it took to have a clean home. I learned that there were people there to support me, but one of the biggest understanding and learning's was that no matter if we fought, at the end of the day there was a Mom and Dad, brothers and sisters, a family that still loved me.

School was a horrible time for me. I struggled with the learning part as much as the social part. Having FASD was like going into a race and someone put an extra hundred pound weight on me. It wasn't fair. I woke up everyday feeling like I was headed off to bang my head against the wall and get nowhere. I couldn't concentrate or remember. This made doing schoolwork very difficult. My dad would sit down with me and try to help. Many times it ended up with me walking away frustrated and not getting my work done. My parents and I didn't realize that the problem was my teacher was teaching me one way to do the work and my parents were teaching me differently. I could not explain it properly and all that came out was "that's not right". I would return to school the next day and have nothing to hand in. I started to feel very alone and misunderstood. The kids thought I was silly and weird. My teachers took my lack of understanding and struggle with memory as lack of effort and no focusing. I didn't understand that a lot of the struggles were struggles many individuals with FASD have. The issue of my maturity level not being up to my chronological age. The struggles of not being able to connect things in my head. By high school I was feeling so alone and misunderstood I thought I would go through life as a loner.I got involved in alcohol and drugs for a while because I thought it got me friends but I was wrong because they were not friends at all. It got worse when I found out that my biological parents were both dead when I went to find them. At that time of my life I was very depressed but I knew that Brian and Christine and all my brothers and sisters still loved me. By that time they had adopted 9 children. As I found the strength to move forward in life I realized I had been truly blessed. It may seem hard to see how I would feel blessed after going through struggling in school and losing my biological parents and having addiction issues and living with FASD. I feel all these things have made me who I am today and helped to see life in a different vein. I now realize that I am a strong young man with many talents and a lot to offer. I would not change anything in my life not even having FASD. I have had the opportunity to mentor others living with FASD and do motivational speaking about living successfully with FASD. In the past as much as I tried to keep people at a distance I couldn't. I have come to realize that there were people who cared and loved me unconditionally. People who took a scared little boy and protected him and showed him being part of a family was like. January 30 1981 thing was the day that changed my life and for that I'd like to say thank you and I love you Brian and Christine Himmelreich my parents.

Myles is a recipient of the Canadian Starfish Award honouring those who have made a substantial contribution to the FASD community. He is a contributing author to several books including, "Finding Perspective... Raising Successful Children Affected by FASD." A movie about his life, "Realities and Possibilities: The Myles Himmelreich Story" was developed by the Saskatchewan Prevention Institute© in 2009. In this DVD, he openly shares his struggles and triumphs with honesty and humour. He is an internationally renowned keynote speaker. His lectures have been well received by professional, parent, and youth groups. Mr. Himmelreich is employed as a Mentor to other youth and adults diagnosed within FASD. To see Myles in action, go to www.obdtriage.com under Speakers. To order a copy of the DVD, please contact: info@preventioninstitute.sk.ca

A Braided Cord Helps Me Be The Best I Can Be

By Ms. Liz Kulp

I was born with FASD and adopted, my birth mother died when I was a tiny baby so part of my early life was in foster care. In my fourth foster care home I moved in with my future adoptive parents. They say they were so happy to have a tiny baby and it didn't matter to them that I was sick and very little. At five months I was just 11 pounds and was not keeping my food down. They say I did not look at people or roll over or smile yet. I was very lucky because I had three adults who loved me, our neighbour, Nancy took care of me during the day when mom or dad went to work so I always had someone to love me and was able to stay close to home.

My parents kept me very busy. I had a very happy life until first grade when I learned I could not learn how other children learn. My teacher was really mean and it only made things worse. It is when I started getting headaches. I know now at age 25 that these were tension headaches—but it took until this year to figure it all out. I do physical therapy to manage them, which is much better than having my kidneys fail because of all the pain medication I took for all those years. People need to know that if you have FASDs you may have many little things that don't work and one little change in medicine or the surrounding area can mess you up big time.

When I was ten my mom started to homeschool me and teach me so I could remember. I knew I was safe and comfortable with my family and that made learning easier. With Mom I was able to learn like other students because she put me in the middle of the learning and made me do things I didn't always want to, but she made it fun. Sometimes I made her crazy because I was hard to teach. We also did vitamins and only ate really good food. We also did neurodevelopment exercises every day to help strengthen my brain, calm me down and make learning easier. I believe all that good food and exercise helped me survive my early adult years after I graduated from a public high school. I wish we could have known about FASDs before I was 12 because I know Mom and Dad would have done whatever it took to help me grow and maybe I would have understood my disability better by age 18 when I decided I was an adult and could do what I wanted.

My parents did everything they knew how to do to make my life better and I know now when I am with other young adults with FASDs how lucky I was to have all the extra help in music, arts, cooking, and adventures. Today live on my own and manage my home because of all they shared with me. I learn from life experience and if I am involved in things I learn how to do them. My mother still helps me with managing my money and errands, as I still do not drive a car, but hope to someday. And someday marry and have a child. But I also know that each piece will take time and it is better to have it right than all messed up. Knowing who I am and how my body and brain works helps me to be patient. Having five years of hardship made a big impact on me. I love friendships and I chose the wrong people to have fun with and the wrong kind of fun. Relationships are important to me so the one thing I would recommend to new adoptive families is to build relationships with GOOD people who enjoy doing fun things with your child and are willing to stay in their life for the long haul and when they get older and are going to die to add another person to already be able to take their place. Keeping things in a structure makes my life more manageable. When I wrote Braided Cord I wanted people to know that it takes a lot of people braiding into my life to help me without overwhelming me. And if I only had one person in my braid I would overwhelm that people.

I am not embarrassed about my disability. It is a part of who I am and my parents accepted it and me. When you live in a world different from others it can be very frustrating for everyone. Mom says adopting a child with FASDs is a big adventure in extreme parenting and it has given her and Dad strength. Sometimes the way I think makes me angry, but then other times I love my beautiful mind and the way I see the world. Life is hard with FASDs but that's okay because life is hard for everyone—you just trying.

Since she was diagnosed with FASDs at age twelve, Liz Kulp has told the world of what it is like to live with this invisible disability. She is the Gold Award Winner, Best Contributing Young Author & Adult Non-Fiction Life Challenges of the Mom's Choice Awards, Canadian Starfish Award, Minnesota Foster Care Association's Adopted Child of the Year, and the 2011 Outstanding Young Leader. Her books, "Braided Cord—Tough Times In and Out—the journey of a young women through adult transition into stability" "My Invisible World—My Brother, His Disability and His Service Dog—by an 11 year old sibling of a boy with FASD", Our Fascinating Journey and almost Best I Can Be can be found the website www.betterendings.org. Liz's book, "Best I Can Be" is now translated into Russian and Ukrainian as an ebook for the people of those countries.

You can find Liz Kulp's and many other young people's success stories at **www.fosterclub.com.**

Katei's Letter

By Ms. Katei S.

Katei is currently with her parents until the family is able to find her a supported living placement with an agency that understands individuals living with FASD. She will require daily support and supervision for her lifetime. She enjoys movies, animals, volunteering in the community, amd aspires to make her own movies. In the past, she has been suicidal requiring hospitalization, and has benn arrested for property damage when she ran away from home and has assaulted her siblings in the past.

My name is Katei. I have FSD. I am 18 and a adult. I work in a store with help my mom and dad + brothers + sister love me even when I ran away + got drunk. I know getting drunk is not the answr but I feel bad sometimes about myself but my boyfriend likes me any way. I got depresd + mad becus people always tell me what to do.

I hope I will be a movie star one day.

Stay strong. you have to beleve.

Katei S.

A Step into FASD with Justin Schafer

By Mr. Justin Schafer

My name is Justin Schafer and I have Fetal Alcohol Spectrum Disorder. I'm adopted and knowing that I'm adopted was something that I had to come to terms with. Not knowing my biological parents was something that I thought to be hard to accept. Overtime I realized that my mother and father along with my sisters and brother were the family that I did have and accepting that at a young age was hard at first but easier as I grew up. I understood that my brother and I had the same biological mother, but different biological father, who made me feel that blood connection to him, for even today I hold him close to my heart and grasp the fact he is the only known blood relation I have. I will always love my family for everything they have given me and stuck through with me through these long years.

I grew up in Okotoks, AB where I attended kindergarten to Grade 12. School was a kind of hard life academically and personally. There were plenty of hardships trying to grasp the education that's given and trying to understand what's being taught. Having FASD was hard because learning things took me twice as long to understand and grasp. Nevertheless, I'm given the resources from the schools I went to, to help me better grasp what is being taught to me.

Growing up was something that I believe to be extremely hard. Knowing that I have FASD is one thing, but grasping the fact that what comes with the disability is the rest of the battle. I am a young adult who knows that life is what you make it, and through the tears and struggles I have been through, there was nothing that I didn't accept to be true about myself. I, like everyone else, am an intelligent individual who does know right from wrong. But here's the catch, It takes you once or twice to learn not to do your mistake again, where it takes me almost twice the amount to know that my mistake was wrong. Some say it's a thrill, others say it's just pure insanity. I say it's me learning in my own way and showing others that just because I take longer to learn something, doesn't mean I'm stupid and can't learn something. It means that I am doing things in my own way and just doing them at my own pace.

Some youth say that being a child with not enough money to go see a favorite concert, or can't go out to see your friends because your parents say you have to do your homework instead, is a hard life. I'm sorry but if I were in their shoes I would be so happy my parents kept me in doors because I feared sometimes to even go to school when I was younger.

I was bullied from grade five to Grade eleven. There were days I feared for my very life coming to school because I didn't know if I would get my ass kicked and not be able to walk home. Because I was different, I didn't fit in, and because I didn't fit in, I didn't belong. For my entire high school career, I was an outcast and I spent time with all my friends who were also outcasts and accepted me for me. There was not a day that went by that I didn't seem to feel drifted further and further away from school life. I was shoved into bully circles, pushed into lockers, downgraded, an insulted from so many people who believed I shouldn't even be showing my face at school. On January 30th, 2009, I attempted suicide, and was placed in the Calgary Rockyview General Hospital. Tears filled my eyes as I looked my mother in the eyes and said I was done, I didn't want to live anymore because I was so hurt from the pain I was going through every day, the things I did to hurt people, and the aggression that I was going through with family. To this very day two and a half years later I look upon January 30th, 2009 and say it was a large stepping stone in my life that gave me the courage to say I am someone who hit rock bottom and moved on from it to become someone better and more developed.

My biggest help was my parents, my friends, and my teachers at school. They showed me that there was more to life than just sitting behind a desk, or lying in bed, or making a goal in soccer. They taught me that every action I made had an equal reaction, to take responsibility and to learn from them, and to come clean with my problems and to be myself in everything that I did. They taught me to know I am somebody and not just another face on this planet. Most of all they gave me the courage to do the things that I loved the most.

I used to think of all the things I hated about myself but lately I have thought of the things that I am proud of. I have accomplished many things that to myself very significant. I am a musician and have been for 9 years, I love to play the guitar because it gives me that special feeling of giving out my ideas and opinions through a talent that I possess.

If you are looking to adopt a child with FASD this will be a road that you will experience with multiple twists and turns. It will be an adventure to look through the eyes of a child with a disability that to this very day shakes the world with wonder and awe. There are difficulties and there are strugles but in the end there is something that you and your child will come to understand that is a new found love that family can expereince together. We are gifted children and we are here today to show you that even though we have this disability, we also have the ability to understand and learn right from wrong just like everyone else.

*Justin is 20 years of age and lives in Calgary, Alberta, Canada. He is a first year student attending The Southern Alberta Institute of Technology (SAIT) studying Radio Broadcasting. He was an Air Cadet for 5 years in the 187 Foothills RCACS in Okotoks/High River Alberta. Justin is a talented musician and is currently teaching guitar and writes his own music. He enjoys public speaking to encourage others to find their own path and feel good about themselves. To hear Justin's musical works, please see his self-designed website at: **www.wix.com/justinschafer/schafermusic**.*

Chapter Ten

Next Steps

Recommendations

- Establish a regular physician preferably that has expertise in FASD or that is willing to be educated in this area. Speak to the diagnostic physician or team staff directly, if possible.

- Please do not stop prescribed medication without consulting with the prescribing or current physician. Medication may be a life-long necessity in conjunction with other learning strategies.

- Ask questions and familiarize yourselves with funding from provincial/state and federal government agencies. This may include programs such as Child Disability Benefit tax credits, Family Support for Children with Disabilities, Supports for Permanency (Post Adoption Supports). Inquire about the eligibility criteria and types of supports available to your child and family.

- Investigate Adult Disabilities programs and funding eligibility criteria in your area as well.

- A medical and/or cognitive testing review will very likely be required in two to five years from the initial appointment as recommended by the diagnostic physician and FASD team. These assessments may be costly and should be considered and included in your funding support agreements.

Based on other parents' experiences, your family will likely require specialized supports:

- Regular shared care (respite) and everyone caring for your child will need to have information and understanding of your child as you do, and are willing to "mimic" your rules and structure.

- Therapeutic support for your child and your family at some point in time, and this support may be intermittent over the years. It is essential to retain a professional that has extensive training in FASD specifically to avoid further complications.

- Talk to other parents who have adopted a child diagnosed with FASD as well as other special needs children, and be cautious of what you read in outdated books or websites on FASD.

- Your child will likely require major dental care (possibly orthodontics), hearing, and regular vision check-ups. Some children may arrive malnourished and require a consult with a Nutritionist as well.

- It would be beneficial to have a referral from your doctor to an Occupational Therapist for Sensory Processing (Integration) Assessment and prescribed intervention techniques if required.

- Although supervision needs vary between patients, it is highly likely that your child will need structure and supervision required for a younger child. Many families continue to act in a supportive parent role well into adulthood. For some individuals, this type of extensive support is required life-long.

- Do some extra homework such as meeting other parents that are raising or have raised children diagnosed with FASD. Read books (see suggested reading list), adoptive parent blogs, review DVDs and interview professionals that are familiar with FASD prior to meeting the child.

- Remember that due to the "invisibility of the disability," your family and child may not receive the same support by friends, family and professionals as a family living with an observable form of brain dysfunction/injury. Educating others about FASD and how it affects your child and family is paramount in changing other people's attitudes. Once they have a better understanding, they will be ready and willing to help. Tell them what you need from them and don't be afraid to ask for help when you need it.

- For many children, logical and natural consequences may not work due to the misfiring of their brain. Nonetheless, repetitive teaching of concepts, structure, self-esteem building, and strategies that are individualized to your child's abilities can reduce the incidence of problematic behaviours.

- You may want to explore a low-stimulating environment for your child's room based on their sensory integration factors.

- In the event your child has memory problems or is hard on toys due to motor/brain dysfunction, you may want to consider purchasing inexpensive or good second hand toys, games, etc. in anticipation of them possibly being lost or quickly broken.

- Try not to become over reactive and remind yourself that it is not that they won't do what you want them to do, it is likely that they can't or did not fully understand the concept. Try to remind yourself to act with kindness and understanding, the same way you would with someone that has brain dysfunction from Alzheimer's disease for example.

- Have fun teaching your child and think outside the box. Making a pizza together helps teach putting things in order, following directions, working together, patience, and a tasty reward at the end!

- Make sure that you and your spouse/partner are on the same page with your belief systems in how to parent a child with special needs. If one or both of you are firm in your principles of what parenting should be and do not think you could be flexible and willing to accommodate changes, you may consider that you might not be the best match for a child with FASD.

- Connect with a Parent Support Group in your area or on-line before, during and after your adoption process. Almost all Provinces, States and now countries have FASD information groups that are available to provide information, resources and support services.

- If you have other children, talk openly and honestly (if age appropriate) about how having a child with special needs may affect them. How would they deal with them taking or breaking their toy? Are they able to understand that other children have special needs? If so, preparation of all siblings is important in avoiding potential hurt feelings or resentments.

- Be advised that if you are adopting birth siblings or several children at a time, that there is a strong possibility that they could all have a diagnosis within FASD even though they all present very differently.

- Be kind. "If you want others to be happy, practice compassion. If you want to be happy, practice compassion." *The Dalai Lama*.

- Be a terrific and creative role model. This is a chance to really shine in areas you may never have considered before. Think outside the box, demonstrate good manners and live with empathy, and forgiveness.

- Consider what your true feelings are about pregnant women drinking alcohol. Be cautious of making disrespectful or judgmental statements regarding the birth mother in front of your child. Children interpret such comments to mean that they have done something wrong, or that they are somehow bad. As discussed earlier, no woman drinks alcohol in a pregnancy on purpose to harm her baby. Discretion and care must be taken when sharing this information with your child at the opportune developmental level.

- Provide as many self-esteem boosters as you can and expect that your child may try out many sports, activities, hobbies, jobs, and friends throughout their life course. There is nothing wrong with having many experiences in life.

- Talk to parents of other forms of organic brain injuries. You may find similarities in strategies and supports.

- Inclusion of your child in well-supported educational settings and community activities provides positive experiences.

- Focus on your child's strengths in personality, abilities, and interests while acknowledging and accommodating their challenges.

- Try to live by the Four Agreements: 1) Be impeccable with your word, 2) Don't take anything personally, 3) Don't make assumptions, and 4) Always do your best.[46]

- In the event that you and your family decide to go ahead with adopting, support services should be accessed immediately to get you started in your journey. Ask about adoption subsidy programs, Children with Disabilities Funding, Medicaid etc. and what they provide.

- Like Forest Gump once said, "Life is like a box of chocolates—you never know what you are going to get." Adopting any child regardless of disabilities means you have to be ready to open up to a realm of possibilities. Any child might become a doctor or a doorman, are they both ok with you?

- If you have taken everything into consideration and you, or any member of your family, do not feel comfortable adopting a child diagnosed, or suspected to be living with FASD, it is in the best interest of the child and your family to say "no". Saying no to an adoption is just as much a loving statement as yes.

In closing…

- Evaluations for FASD and other medical possibilities should be completed *prior* to an adoption.

- If you have already adopted and have concerns about your child, locate the FASD diagnostic clinic near you and contact your provincial or state FASD support agencies or groups for guidance.

- Remember that FASD is a medical disposition and that most often, challenging behaviours, are inherently related to the child's whole body disorder.

- Get written copies of everything. Interview the adoption agency's representative / worker specifically about if, and how they acquire information from the birth parents and families of origin regarding possible substance use in her pregnancy. Ask lots of questions expressly about the family and history of alcohol and/or drug use and related lifestyles. Insist on realistic information about the child's medical, social, emotional and behavioural history to date. If they are not sure of the procedure, please suggest they contact the OBD Triage Institute directly, or the local FASD Diagnostic Clinic for assistance in how to appropriately gather such information and what is necessary for diagnosis.

- Be sure to ask specifically about what potential medical treatment, follow up, various therapies, dental work, and resources are available. Inquire as to costs and eligibility criteria for funding. For children that have a pre-existing diagnosis within FASD, request a copy of the diagnosis and summary in its entirety and request an appointment with the FASD Diagnostic Clinic to discuss the diagnosis with the medical team.

- Be sure to instil as much balance between tending to your adopted child, your other children, and marriage / partner. Raising children with FASD takes patience, understanding, structure, acceptance, compassion, optimism and flexibility.

- Humour is the best medicine! Find humour in every day in any way you can, and share it with others. Explore your child's sense of humour. You may have a comedian on your hands!

- Don't forget to look after yourself too!

All of this information may sound daunting, but to adopt a child with FASD is to adopt a child who needs more unconditional love, attention, patience, and hope than many other potential parents are able to give. Your family's dedication and commitment no matter what, is an extraordinary gift. It is a challenge, but one that could bring lifelong fulfillment to a special needs child.

Over the years I have often been asked from my experience, "What are the common denominators in families that have been successful in raising children with FASD?" The answers are still the same. They have faith, and a sense of humour. They tell their children that they can do whatever they set out to do regardless of difficulties. They focus on abilities while acknowledging and supporting areas where they struggle. Moreover, they truly get that their child has a medical problem that comes with difficult behaviours not unlike other forms of developmental disability. As hard as it is sometimes, they remember that behaviour is not an intended provocation towards them personally. They appreciate the invisibility of the disability and how hard it is to be different from other kids, even a little. Not that life has always been easy. The individuals and families that have courageously shared their stories for you in this book have made that crystal clear. Regardless of your decision, please never lose faith, hope, and humour in all you do. Good Luck!

"There are two ways to live: you can live as if nothing is a miracle;
you can live as if everything is a miracle."

Albert Einstein

Appendix A

Medical Models of Diagnosis

1) The FASD 4-Digit Diagnostic Code, S.J. ASTLEY Revised (2004).

THE 4-DIGIT DIAGNOSTIC CODE was initially developed in 1997. (Susan J. Astley, Ph.D., and Sterling K. Clarren, M.D. Diagnostic Prevention Network. University of Washington).

The four digits in the Code reflect the magnitude of expression of the four key diagnostic features of FAS in the following order: (1) growth deficiency, (2) the FAS facial features, (3) central nervous system (CNS) damage/dysfunction, and (4) prenatal alcohol exposure. The magnitude of expression of each feature is ranked independently on a 4-point Likert scale with 1 reflecting complete absence of the FAS feature and 4 reflecting a strong "classic" presence of the FAS feature. The 4-Digit Diagnostic Code has been used to diagnose over 2,000 patients in the FAS DPN clinics to date. A patient's 4-Digit Diagnostic Code is derived after a thorough evaluation by an interdisciplinary team of professionals. The team typically includes a physician, psychologist, occupational therapist, speech-language pathologist, social worker, and family advocate.[49]

One Example of FAS

				3	4	4	4		
significant	significant	definite 4			X	X	X	4	high risk
moderate	moderate	probable 3	X					3	some risk
mild	mild	possible 2						2	Unknown
none	none	unlikely 1						1	no risk
Growth Deficiency	FAS Facial Features	CNS Damage	Growth	Face	CNS	Alcohol		Prenatal Alcohol	

Degree to which each factor is present is ranked on a 4-point Likert scale: 1 = complete absence of feature; to 4 = full, classic presentation. Results generate a 4-digit diagnostic "code:"

The 4-Digit Diagnostic Code reflects the magnitude of expression of four key diagnostic components of FAS in the order growth, facial phenotype, CNS damage/dysfunction and alcohol exposure. Each component is measured on a 4-point Likert scale, thus producing **256** possible combinations of 4-Digit Diagnostic Codes.[50]

Another Medical Model

2) Institute of Medicine – 5 possible diagnoses

- FAS (Fetal Alcohol Syndrome) with confirmed alcohol exposure
- FAS (Fetal Alcohol Syndrome) without confirmed alcohol exposure
- Predicting Outcomes (pFAS) (some, not all features of Fetal Alcohol Syndrome)
- ARND (Alcohol Related Neurobehavioural Disorder)
- ARBD (Alcohol Related Birth Defects)

Four groups of criteria:

- Growth deficiencies
- Characteristic facial phenotype
- Central nervous system damage/dysfunction
- Alcohol exposure in utero

Another Model

3) Hoyme's "Clarification of IOM guides" (2005) – 6 possible diagnoses

- FAS (Fetal Alcohol Syndrome) with confirmed alcohol exposure
- FAS (Fetal Alcohol Syndrome) without confirmed alcohol exposure
- Partial FAS with confirmed alcohol exposure
- Partial FAS without confirmed alcohol exposure
- ARND (Alcohol Related Neurobehavioural Disorder)
- ARBD (Alcohol Related Birth Defects)
- 4 groups of criteria IOM's 4 groups of criteria + rankings 3 groups of criteria (modified IOM)

Three groups of criteria:

1. Growth and structural development

2. Neuropsychological, intellectual, and social development

3. Maternal risk factors

Appendix B

OBD Diagnostic Interpretation of Abilities Clinic (DIAC)©

Organic Brain Dysfunction

Upon completion of the medical evaluation and **verification** of a diagnosis within Fetal Alcohol Spectrum Disorder, a Diagnostic Interpretation of Abilities Session is then obtainable. The DIAS clinics provide a detailed explanation of the individual's respective medical diagnosis including various potential prenatal teratogenic exposures, genetic and hereditary factors and social history. Further, identify the patient's *specific* physical, sensory, and cognitive variables that may *translate* to what appears to be wilful or uncooperative behaviour when in fact, it is as a direct result of their medical disposition. The ultimate goal is to enhance understanding of FASD as a whole body disorder and offer strength based approaches to reducing frustration for the patient and the family and professionals working with them.

Once these issues are acknowledged, prevention strategies and intervention techniques are suitably designed utilizing the **OBD 3 Steps Plan of Action!** by focusing on individual strengths, interests and abilities in order to create successes in all areas of their life course. The aim is to assist individuals, families, Courts, Social Services and community agencies in developing appropriate planning within the home or residential environment, academic/vocational settings and recreational activities.

The sessions consist of a two-hour Power Point presentation designed specifically regarding the child, youth or adult. Invitations are extended to all persons living and/or working with the individual including Caregivers, Extended Family, Mentors, Respite providers, Teachers, Coaches, Principals, Classroom Aides, Probation Officers, Lawyers, Employment Preparation Staff or Employers, Foster Care Support Workers, Children's Services Workers, Persons with Developmental Disabilities (P.D.D.) and Assured Income for the Severely Handicapped (A.I.S.H.) service providers, Youth Workers, Group Home and/or agency staff, Therapists, Addictions Treatment Counsellors, and Justice representatives.

The clinics are conducted within the community setting or through virtual online communication options.

The structure of these clinics is as follows:

- To review the particular **physiological** issues and identification of the patient's physical findings (243 physical possibilities are reviewed) that may translate to challenges for the individual, and present to others with the *appearance* of intentionally inappropriate behaviours.

- Identify specific **sensory integration** issues that may cause frustration for the individual and challenges for them in a classroom, home, treatment or work environment.

- To provide an accurate explanation of the overall **cognitive and executive functioning abilities** with the focus on strengths while acknowledging their challenges and the correlation between processing abilities and challenging behavioural issues.

- Explore **social history** and discuss the potential impact of any previous childhood maltreatment and social history factors as they pertain to strategy development.

- By utilizing the **OBD 3** Steps Plan of Action! demonstrate which issues are likely responsible for the manifestation of the current behaviours of collective concern and design patient-specific prevention methods and intervention strategies to reduce the frustration level for the patient and incidence of the inappropriate behaviour(s).

- As a working group, encourage discussion and develop suggestions and recommendations for each participant with the collective goal to modify (if required) the home, school, therapeutic and/or recreational environments in order to provide the child/youth or adult with the best possible chance of success throughout their life course. By including all persons involved, our objectives are to develop relationships and provide consistency in all areas of service delivery.

OBD *Patient* Diagnostic Interpretation of Abilities Sessions ©

Where appropriate with overall functioning and timing, Patient clinics are offered. It provides an explanation of their medical diagnosis by visual, auditory and tactile design. It is created specifically to the patient's learning style and are focused on identification of the individual's strengths and abilities while acknowledging physical, sensory and functioning issues. Other areas that are addressed are academic placement, employment options, birth control, anger management/therapeutic interventions, relationships, recreation, substance abuse and prescribed medication. The patient is involved in constructing the ongoing process thereby promoting follow through of their personal goals and provision of well-matched support services for areas of need.

Appendix C

Care of Babies experiencing Withdrawal Symptoms

Prolonged, high pitched cry, irritability

- Cuddles and dummies (pacifiers) are comforting.
- Hold your baby close to you.
- Try to keep his/her arms and legs bent.
- They may like to be wrapped or carried in a sling.
- Reduce light and noise. Strong smells may also upset your baby.
- Bathing your baby in warm water may help.
- Dry him or her gently.
- Talk softly to your baby.
- Try sitting baby up facing you.

Sleeplessness

- Reduce noise and light.
- Humming or soft, gentle music may help.
- Rocking may be soothing.
- Avoid patting or touching your baby too much.
- Don't jiggle or shake baby.

Poor feeding or vomiting

- Support your baby's chin and cheeks to increase his/her sucking ability.
- Feed in quiet, calm surroundings with minimal noise and disturbance.
- Feed baby slowly, stop several times during a feed to "wind" (burp).
- Feed baby small amounts more often. And allow time for resting between sucking. Clean any vomit from the skin.

Sneezing, stuffy nose or breathing fast

- Keep baby's nose and mouth clean.
- Avoid wrapping your baby too tightly.

Excessive sucking of fist

- Make sure that your baby is not hungry.
- Use scratch mitts to prevent baby damaging his/her skin.
- Give your baby a dummy (pacifier) to suck for comfort, but not instead of a feed.

Trembling, Stiffness

- Handle your baby slowly and gently.
- Change baby's position frequently.
- A warm bath can help to reduce stiffness. Try laying your baby on his/her side and bring hips and knees forward to reduce stiffness. Place a soft towel between the knees. Always watch your baby if lying on his/her side.
- To control trembling, hold baby's hands across their chest, shoulders forward.
- Reduce light and noise.

Sore bottom

- Change your baby's nappy frequently.
- Use a barrier cream.

Panicking when woken

- Approach baby quietly and calmly.
- Wake gently by stroking and talking softly.
- Remove bed covers slowly, holding your baby's limbs.

*If your baby seems to be panting (even when asleep), becomes pale or his/her skin colour appears blue, call an ambulance (emergency services) immediately. 911, 999

- Make sure your baby is kept in very quiet and calm surroundings, no bright lights or loud sounds that might upset your baby.
- Make sure no one smokes near your baby, keep the air fresh but warm.
- Hold your baby as much as you can, the baby will cry less and feed better if they have 'skin-to-skin' contact.
- Use a dummy or pacifier ('soothers')... unless you are breastfeeding.

- Move and handle your baby very gently; try giving them a gentle massage.

- Change your baby's clothes frequently, especially if they sweat a lot.

- Avoid getting your baby too hot.

- Regularly check and change your baby's nappy (diaper).

- Use a barrier cream around the baby's bottom area to help prevent any skin damage.

- Feed your baby on demand; frequent small feeds are normally better.

- Keep a record of all the feeds your baby takes so that the midwife or nurse can check whether your baby is feeding well enough and putting on enough weight.

If your baby has a convulsion (seizure) you should put him/her in a safe place and call for help immediately. It is important that you or others **do not smoke** in the house or near your baby. It is not recommended that you sleep with your baby during problems with symptoms of withdrawal.

See your doctor regularly to ensure that the baby is gaining weight appropriately and for overall checkups as suggested by your physician. Used with permission. **www.northdevonhealth.nhs.uk**

Read more at:

http://wiki.answers.com/Q/What_is_auditory_sensitivity#ixzz1Nrh4gwrf.

Recommended Readings in Alphabetical Order

A star in front of the title indicates the book's content is written and/or contributed to by parents and/or individuals living with FASD

*Braided Cord – Tough Times In and Out (2010). Liz Kulp.

Children With Prenatal Alcohol and/or Other Drug Exposure: Weighing the Risks of Adoption. (1995). Edelstein, S. Washington, DC: CWLA Press.

*Families at Risk (1994). Jodee Kulp Better Endings New Beginnings Publisher.

FAS: Parenting Children Affected by Fetal Alcohol Syndrome. A Guide for Daily Living. 2nd edition revised. (1999). Editor: Susan Graefe.

Fetal Alcohol Syndrome – A Guide for Families and Communities. (1999). A.P. Streissguth.

*Finding Perspective... Raising Successful Children Affected by Fetal Alcohol Spectrum Disorder. (2005). Liz Lawryk.

*Forgetful Frankie – The Worlds Greatest Rock Skipper, Fetal Alcohol Spectrum Disorder. (2009). Jill Bobula, Katherine Bobula, Joe Goski, and Rob Hall.

*Hard Issues for Parents of Adolescents and Adults with FASD. Author: Jan Lutke. http://www.fasdconnections.ca/id27.htm

*Iceburg Newsletter. http://www.fasiceberg.org/newsletters/Vol16Num2_Jun2006.htm

*Journey to Life. (1986). Jodee Kulp.

*Letters to Our Children, Letters from Our Children: Living with Fetal Alcohol Syndrome and Related Effects. (2000). Editors: Dorothy Badry and Liz Lawryk.

*Living with FASD. (Informative Newsletter). FASD Saskatchewan Support Network of Saskatchewan Inc. Multiple Authors. Saskatchewan, Canada.

*Long Way To Simple – 50 Years of Ideas to Live, Love and Laugh as a person with FASDs. (2008). Stephen Neafcy, Jodee Kulp.

*My Invisible World – Life with My Brother, His Disability and His Service Dog. The story of a typical sibling living with a brother with FASDs.(2009). Morasha Winokur. She wrote this at 11 years old! (www.thechancerchronicles.com)

*Our FAScinating Journey (2002, 2004, 2011). Jodee Kulp. Keys to Brain Potential Along the Path of Prenatal Brain Injury.

Parenting with FASD – Challenges, Strategies and Supports. (2005). D. Rutman, C. La Berge and D. Wheway.

Raising A Sensory Smart Child. The Definitive Handbook for Helping Your Child with Sensory Integration Issues. (2005). Lindsey Biel and Nancy Peske.

Reaching Out to Children with FAS/FAE: A Handbook for Teachers, Counselors, and Parents Who Live and Work with Children Affected by Fetal Alcohol Syndrome. (1994). Diane Davis.

*Speaking and Learning the Fasd Way. Carol McAndrew.

*The Best I Can Be – Living with Fetal Alcohol Spectrum Disorders. (2011- 8th Edition). Liz Kulp. Better Endings Best Beginnings Publisher.

The Challenge of Fetal Alcohol Syndrome – Overcoming Secondary Disabilities. (1997). Editors: A.P. Streissguth and J. Kanter.

*The Long Way to Simple – 50 years of Living, Loving and Laughing as a Person with FASD. (2008). Stephen Neafcy.

The Out-of-Sync Child – Recognizing and Coping with Sensory Integration Dysfunction. (2005- 2nd Edition). Carol Stock Kranowitz.

*The Whitest Wall. Author: (2008). Jodee Kulp.

*Tiny Titan – Journey of Hope *Mom's Choice Award by the Just for Mom Foundation. (2006). Ann Yurcek.

*Trying Differently Rather Than Harder: Fetal Alcohol Spectrum Disorders. (2002). Diane Malbin.

Websites and FASD Support Groups

Canada

Canadian Center on Substance Abuse **http://www.ccsa.ca/fasgen.htm**

Health Canada **http://www.hc-sc.gc.ca/hppb/childhood-youth/cyfh/fas/ resources.html**

FAS World Canada **http://fasworld.com/home.ihtml**

Health Canada **http://www.fas-saf.com/**

FAS Resource List **http://thearc.org/misc/faslist.html**

Finding Hope **http://findinghope.knowledge.ca/home.html**

Government of BC **http://www.mcf.gov.bc.ca/child_protection/fas/index.html**

FAS support network of BC **http://www.fetalalcohol.com/frame-home.htm**

Registered Disability Savings Plan Factsheet
http://www.rdsp.com/upload/RDSP/RDSP_Factsheet.pdf

Fetal Alcohol Spectrum Disorder & Justice **http://www.fasdjustice.on.ca/**

Directory: FAS Parent Support Groups - Canada, depts.washington.edu/ fadu/Support.Groups.CA.html. Directory, contact info.

Alberta

Alberta Service Agencies **http://www.informalberta.ca/public/common/ index_ClearSearch.do**

Government of Alberta Education **http://education.alberta.ca/teachers/ resources/fasd.aspx**

Alberta Children's Services **http://www.child.gov.ab.ca/whatwedo/fas/ page.cfm?pg=index**

Lakeland Centre for FASD **http://www.lcfasd.com/**

The **OBD** Triage Institute **www.obdtriage.com**

British Columbia

FASD Support Resources in B.C. **http://www.mcf.gov.bc.ca/fasd/ assessment.htm**

FAS Resource Society, c/o Sunny Hill Health Centre for Children, 3644 Slocan St., Vancouver, V5M 3E8, 604-467-5591.

Groundwork Press **http://www.groundworkpress.com**

The Assante Centre for FASD **http://www.asantecentre.org/**

FAS/E Support Network of B.C., 13279 72nd Ave., Surrey V3W 2N5. 604-507-6675; info@fetalalcohol.com, **www.fetalalcohol.com**. Support, consultation and training across Canada. 5-day training courses in Surrey. Founded 1989 by Jan Lutke, Donna Wheway, Sandi Berg and Karen Kinsey.

Prince George, B.C. FAS Network, Northern Family Health Society, 1154 3rd Ave., Prince George V2L 3E5, postmaster@nfhs-pg.org, **www.nfhs-pg. org/home.html**. FAS community development tools, action committees, FAS research. Marlene Thio-Watts, 250-561-2689, twatts@uniserve.com.

Project Save, info@fasdconnections.ca, **www.fasdconnections.ca**. A support group for parents of adolescents and adults with FASD, providing parents with tools to help them support their adolescent and adult children. Groups meet monthly in Surrey, B.C. and Ottawa, Ont.

Society of Special Needs Adoptive Parents (SNAP), 445-5525 West Boulevard, Vancouver BC V6M 3W6, 604-687-3114, **www.snap.bc.ca**, info@snap.bc.ca

Manitoba

FASD Support Services and Contacts **http://www.gov.mb.ca/healthychild/ fasd/contacts.html**

AS/E Program, **www.mts.net/~childfam/fetalalc.htm**. FAS support group, monthly meetings, library. Child/Family Resource Center, Cranberry Portage MB.

FAS/FAE Interagency Program, 476 King St., #49, Winnipeg R2W 3Z5. Deborah Kacki, 204-582-8658.

Fetal Alcohol Family Association of Manitoba, 210-500 Portage Ave., Winnipeg R3C 3X1, 204-786-1847, fafam@mts.net, **www.fafam.ca**. Executive Director: Leilani Buschau. Providing advocacy, support and education to Manitoba families and professionals. "Circle of Friends" newsletter.

Ontario

Canadian Centre on Substance Abuse, 75 Albert St., #300, Ottawa K1P 5E7. Karen Palmer, librarian, FAS Information Service, 1-800-559-4514; 613-235-4048, ext. 223, fas@ccsa.ca, **www.ccsa.ca/index.asp**. FAS support groups across the country,

Family Helper – Adoption and FASD. Robin Hilborn. **http://www. familyhelper.net/**

FAS Network, Hamilton/Toronto area, Bruce Ritchie, 905-679-2866, netstorm@acbr.com. Margaret Sprenger, Mississauga, 905-822-0733.

FAS Treatment and Education Centre, Jill Dockrill, 194 Foster Ave., Belleville K8N 3P9, 613-968-8129, jillfastec@netscape.net.

Fetal Alcohol Spectrum Disorder Group of Ottawa. Support and education for parents and professionals on the effects of fetal alcohol. Meets the first Tuesday of the month, Oct. through June, at 7 p.m., Children's Hospital of Eastern Ontario. Facilitated by Elspeth Ross and Dr. Viginia Bourget, psychologist, 613-737-1122, 613-446-4144, rosse@ncf.ca. (Formerly at www.ncf.ca/fasao.) - Feb. 18, 2007

FASAT (Ontario), FAS Assistance and Training, home.golden.net/~fasat. Parent support groups in southern Ontario; facts; myths; FAQ; does your child have FAS. Chris Margetson, Guelph, Ont.

FASworld Canada, Bonnie Buxton, Brian Philcox, fasworldcanada@rogers.com, www.fasworld.com. For parents, professionals and individuals living with FAS. National organization strives to reduce FA disorders and their impact, working with health units, family support groups and other organizations who form chapters.

FASworld Toronto (see FASworld Canada). Public support and education. Monthly meetings at St. Michael's Hospital, Toronto. Training sessions for professionals and parents dealing with FAS-afflicted children.

Healthy Generations Family Support Program, Sioux Lookout. Judy Kay, 807-737-2214, fasfas@sl.lakeheadu.ca.

Motherisk Program, **www.motherisk.org**. Information on effects of alcohol; lab tests on babies; FAS assessments at The Hospital for Sick Children, Toronto, 416-813-6780.

MotherRisk – Alcohol and Substance Use Helpline, www.motherisk.org/ alcohol/index.php3. Hospital for Sick Children, Toronto. Toll-free 877-327-4636, open M-F, 9-5, for questions on alcohol or drug use during pregnancy. Doctors may also wish to consult with the team of experts, including pharmacologists, toxicologists, neurologists and paediatricians.

Quebec

SAFERA info@safera.qc.ca, www.safera.qc.ca. Support group founded by

Louise Morin and Luc Roy, adoptive parents of a girl with FAS.

Canadian Centre on Substance Abuse **www.ccsa.ca/.../ccsa-DirectoryFASD-20081103.pdf**

Saskatchewan

SK: Saskatchewan Fetal Alcohol Support Network, 510 Cynthia St., Saskatoon SK S7L 7K7, 306-975-0884, 1-866-673-3276, fas. esupportnetwork@sasktel.net, **www.skfasnetwork.ca**. Information, support and links to services for families and individuals with FASD and to professionals. Help to parent/caregiver support groups across the province.

North West Territories

Support and Resources **http://www.hlthss.gov.nt.ca/english/services/fetal_alcohol_spectrum_disorder/default.htm**

FAS Society Yukon (FASSY), Box 31396, Whitehorse Y1A 6K8, 867-393-4948, fascap@yknet.yk.ca.

U.S. Supports

Add National Organization on FAS **http://www.nofas.org/**

Fetal Alcohol and Drug Unit **http://depts.washington.edu/fadu/**

Alaska: Project FACTS **http://www.fasalaska.com/index.html**

Directory: FAS Parent Support Groups – United States, **depts.washington.edu/fadu/Support.Groups.US.html**.

Minnesota: Better Endings, New Beginnings. Joeee & Liz Kulp website: **http://www.betterendings.org/** and **Toolbox for Parents http://www.do2learn.com/disabilities/FASDtoolbox/index.htm**

Arizona: Fasstar Enterprises, Teresa Kellerman, Tucson **www.fasstar.com**. Training and consultation for professionals providing services to individuals prenatally exposed to alcohol.

Arizona: FAS Community Resource Center **http://come-over.to/FASCRC/**

Minnesota: Better Endings, New Beginnings. Joeee & Liz Kulp website: **http://www.betterendings.org/** and Toolbox for Parents **http://www.do2learn.com/disabilities/FASDtoolbox/index.htm**

Washington D.C: National Organization on FAS (NOFAS) **www.nofas.org**.

Maryland: National Institute on Alcohol Abuse and Alcoholism. http://www.niaaa.nih.gov/Pages/default.aspx

Minnesota Organization on Fetal Alcohol Syndrome **http://www.mofas. org/facts/diagnosis.htm**

Oregon: FAS Consultation, Education and Training Services (FASCETS), Diane Malbin, dmalbin@fascets.org, **www.fascets.org**. Support for children, adolescents and adults with FAS.

Families for Russian and Ukrainian Adoption, **www.frua.org**. For families adopting from the former Soviet Union. Chapters throughout the U.S.

Child Welfare Information Gateway, **www.childwelfare.gov**. Information on adopting children with developmental disabilities, caring for special needs children, adoption subsidies, post-adoption services.

Washington: FAS Family Resource Institute, **www.fetalalcoholsyndrome.org**

Washington:FAS Diagnostic and Prevention Network **http://depts. washington.edu/fasdpn/**

Wisconsin: Family Empowerment Network, University of Wisconsin, Madison Medical School, Madison, **www.fammed.wisc.edu/fen** FAS resources, training.

Eastern European

Easter Europe Adoption Coalition, **www.eeadopt.org** For families adopting from Eastern Europe.

Newsletters – Canada

About FASE, FAS/E Support Network of B.C., 13279 72nd Ave., Surrey BC V3W 2N5. Warm line 604-507-6675, info@fetalalcohol.com, **www.fetalalcohol.com**.

Family Groundwork Magazine, SNAP, 101-2780 East Broadway, Vancouver V5M 1Y8. 604-687-3114, 1-800-663-7627, info@snap.bc.ca, **www.snap. bc.ca/groundwork**. "Canada's Magazine for Parenting Children with Challenges." Jennifer Lee, Editor, jennifer@snap.bc.ca. (Ceased publishing, 2007) (Replaced "Special Needs Adoptive Parents Newsletter")

B.C.FAS Resource Society Newsletter, B.C. FAS Resource Society, Sunny Hill Health Centre for Children, 3644 Slocan St., Vancouver, BC V5M 3E8, 604-467-5591.

Living With FAS/E, Saskatchewan Fetal Alcohol Support Network, 510 Cynthia St., Saskatoon SK S7L 7K7, 306-975-0884, toll free: 1-866-673-3276, **http://www.skfasnetwork.ca/**

Manitoba F.A.S. News, Committee on Alcohol and Pregnancy, Manitoba Medical Assn., 125 Sherbrooke St., Winnipeg MB R3C 2B5, 204-786-7565. Nykola Dubenski.

Post-adoption Helper helper@familyhelper.net, **www.familyhelper.net/pa/ phfas.html**. For all post-adoption issues.

Newsletters – U.S.

F.A.S. Times, FAS Family Resource Institute, Box 2525, Lynnwood WA 98036. 253-531-2878, 800-999-3429, vicfas@hotmail.com, **www.fetalalcoholsyndrome.org**. 4/yr.

FAS/E Newsletter, Box 74612, Fairbanks AK 99707, 907-456-1101.

FEN Pen Newsletter, Family Empowerment Network, Madison WI. 608-262-6590, 800-462-5254, **www.fammed.wisc.edu/fen**.

Iceberg, Box 95597, Seattle WA 98145-2597, 206-827-1773, iceberg_fas@yahoo.com Educational newsletter by FAS Information Service.

Eastern European Adoption Coalition, **www.eeadopt.org**

FAS-CA, groups.yahoo.com/group/FAS-CA. California.

FAS-Florida, groups.yahoo.com/group/FAS-Florida. Florida.

FASWorldTexas, groups.yahoo.com/group/FASWorldTexas. Texas.

MO-FetalAlcoholSupportGroup, groups.yahoo.com/group/MO-FetalAlcoholSupportGroup. Missouri.[49]

Glossary of Terms

Abstract concepts – the image of a thing held in the mind.

Abstract thinking – is often thought to develop around the age of 11 in children, includes a sense of space (microscopic space and cosmic space) and time (historical time and future time). Many individuals with a variety of disabilities have difficulty with abstract thinking.

Accutane™ – is a prescription medication to treat acne.

Adaptive behaviour – the ability to meet the age-appropriate standards of personal independence and social responsibility expected of individuals in his/her age and culture.

Adaptive Behavior Composite Score – is a measure of the person's ability to express and comprehend language, behave appropriately in interpersonal situations, understand and use social behaviours, protect him/herself, and care for him/herself, in terms of personal hygiene and domestic independence. It is measured with instruments such as the Vineland Adaptive Behavior Scales, which measure adaptive behaviour in four major domains, Communication, Daily Living Skills, Socialization, and Gross Motor Skills.

Adaptive functioning – is the ability of someone to communicate, employ daily living skills, socialize and use motor skills, and it is generally correlated with the expected skills at a certain age. It refers to how well people cope with the common tasks of daily living. Adaptive functioning is measured against the degree of personal independence expected of someone in his or her particular age group, sociocultural background and community setting. Individuals with FASD often have deficits in adaptive functioning.

Addiction – addiction is a state of dependence caused by habitual use of drugs, alcohol, or other substances or behaviours such as gambling.

Adult Services Worker – supports adults with developmental disabilities who live on their own. Services may include help with housing, transportation, medical services, dental services, financial services, legal support, spiritual support, vocational programs, leisure programs, educational programs, volunteering programs, and counselling and mental health services. The type of services may vary in different regions.

Affect – is the subjective aspect of an emotion considered apart from bodily changes. The term is often used as a name for feeling, emotion, or mood.

Alcohol – a drink containing the substance ethanol, an intoxicating agent in fermented drinks.

Alcohol-Related Birth Defects (ARBD) – specific organ damage resulting from confirmed prenatal alcohol exposure. This term should not be used as an umbrella term or diagnostic term. ARBD constitutes a list of congenital anomalies including malformations and dysplasias and should be used with caution. Persons with congenital anomalies due to prenatal alcohol exposure will likely also have CNS impairment, and therefore be captured in one of the other more appropriate diagnostic criteria.

Alcohol-Related Neurological Disorder – refers to the brain damage caused by recognized alcohol consumption in pregnancy. ARND brain damage is equivalent to brain damage in full fetal alcohol syndrome but lacks growth deficiencies and facial birth defects. This is considered the most common form of FASD.

Alcohol-related Neurodevelopmental Disorder (ARND) – is a term created by the Institute of Medicine (1996), used to describe individuals with confirmed maternal alcohol use, neurodevelopmental abnormalities, a complex pattern of behavioural or cognitive abnormalities inconsistent with developmental level and not explained by genetic background or environment. Problems may include learning disabilities, school performance deficits, inadequate impulse control, social perceptual problems, language dysfunction, abstraction difficulties, mathematics deficiencies, and judgment, memory, and attention problems. Children with this diagnosis do not have growth restriction or the characteristic facial features of prenatal alcohol exposure but do have severe learning and behaviour problems, as well as a confirmed history of alcohol exposure. Children with this diagnosis may require as much support as a child with Fetal Alcohol Syndrome. Studies suggest that that they are at very high risk for problems as they are not observably disabled, but have significant brain impairment that may go unrecognized, and therefore unsupported.

Amphetamine – is a psycho-stimulant drug of the phenethylamine class which produces increased wakefulness and focus in association with decreased fatigue and appetite.

Apgar score – is a method of assessing a newborn immediately after birth. The Apgar score is determined by evaluating the newborn baby on five simple criteria on a scale from zero to two, then summing up the five values thus obtained. The resulting Apgar score ranges from zero to 10. The five criteria are: **A**ppearance, **P**ulse, **G**rimace, **A**ctivity, **R**espiration

Attention – the ability to focus selectively on something, sustaining that focus and shifting it at will; the ability to concentrate and resist distraction.

Attention-deficit/hyperactivity disorder (ADHD) – a persistent pattern of inattention or hyperactivity/impulsivity that is more frequently displayed and more severe than is typically observed in individuals at a comparable level of development. Individuals diagnosed within FASD often meet the diagnostic criteria for ADD and/or ADHD.

Auditory defensiveness – is a tendency to overreact to sounds which are generally considered harmless, or non-irritating to other people.

Autism – a developmental disability significantly affecting verbal and non-verbal communication and social interaction, generally evident before age three. Characteristics often associated with autism are engagement in repetitive activities and stereotyped movements, resistance to environmental change or change in daily routines, and unusual responses to sensory experiences. Autism is a spectrum disorder, which means that there are variations in severity and symptoms for each individual. Diagnoses within the spectrum include: Asperger Syndrome, Rhett syndrome, Fragile X syndrome, and Fetal Alcohol Spectrum Disorders.

Barbiturates – are drugs that act as central nervous system depressants, and can therefore produce a wide spectrum of effects, from mild sedation to total anesthesia. They have addiction potential, both physical and psychological.

Behaviour problems – involves unusual or age-inappropriate behaviour that affects the child's social and academic functioning. For example, unusually high or low activity, impulsivity, distractibility, aggression, poor frustration tolerance, self-regulation difficulties, social and emotional problems.

Birth defect – is a physical or biochemical defect for example, Down syndrome, Fetal Alcohol Syndrome, cleft palate, that is present at birth and may be inherited or environmentally induced, for example, by alcohol consumption.

Central Nervous System (CNS) – The central nervous system (CNS) is comprised of the brain and spinal cord. The CNS receives sensory information from the nervous system and controls the body's responses.

Central Nervous System (CNS) structural abnormalities – involves damage to the brain itself as determined through physical examination/manifestations or a brain scanning technique. They include small head size (microcephaly), seizures, or small or missing brain structures. Individuals with an FASD may have structural brain abnormalities, particularly microcephaly, fewer basal ganglia (associated with motor activity), and small or absent corpus callosum (which carry bundles of nerve fibers that connect the right and left brain hemispheres).

Cerebral Palsy – is a term used to describe a group of chronic conditions affecting body movements and muscle coordination. It is caused by damage to one or more specific areas of the brain, usually occurring during fetal development or infancy. It also can occur before, during or shortly following birth. Cerebral palsy is characterized by an inability to fully control motor function, particularly muscle control and coordination. Some individuals living with FASD may also be diagnosed with Cerebral Palsy.

Childhood maltreatement – describes neglect, emotional, physical, sexual abuses incurred in childhood.

Conceptualizing – requires developing a picture in your mind when the item or concept is not actually in sight. A necessary requirement of conceptualizing is to link the concept to a meaningful time and place, such as a child's birthday.

Concrete concepts – objects or things that are visible, tangible.

Conduct disorder – is a repetitive and persistent pattern of behaviour in which the basic rights of others or major age-appropriate norms or rules are violated. These behaviours may involve aggressive conduct that causes or threatens physical harm to other people or animals, the deliberate destruction of property, deceitfulness or theft, and serious violations of rules. Some individuals with an FASD may be diagnosed with conduct disorder. This could be a co-occurring disorder for some. Others may demonstrate what looks like conduct disorder but may actually be a result of having difficulty understanding rules and requests.

Consequence – is a result or effect of some previous occurrence, an unpleasant result, a conclusion reached by reasoning, the relation between an effect and its cause. For example, "if I steal, I will go to jail."

Co-occurring disorder – refers to the simultaneous existence of a disorder. The disorder/disability is of a type and severity that exacerbates the other conditions, complicates treatment, or interferes with functioning in age-appropriate social roles.

Chronological Age – actual age at the current time, the number of years and days elapsed since birth, for example, six years and nine months old.

Cue – a thing said or done that serves as a signal to the individual to enter or to begin a task.

Depression – is marked by a depressed mood or a loss of interest or pleasure in daily activities consistently for at least 2 weeks. This mood must represent a change from the person's normal mood; social, occupational, educational, or other important functioning must also be negatively impaired by the change in mood. In children and adolescents, this mood may be demonstrated by irritability.

Developmental Age – is determined by a combination of a child or adolescent's physical development (assessed by skeletal maturity or bone age), together with the incorporation of mental, cognitive and emotional maturity. Developmental age is highly individualistic.

Developmental disabilities – are a diverse group of physical, cognitive, psychological, sensory, and speech impairments that begin any time during development up to adulthood.

Diagnosis – is the identification of the nature and cause of anything.

Diagnostic and Statistical Manual of Mental Disorders (DSM-IV) – is the main diagnostic reference of mental health professionals in Canada and the United States. FASD is not a diagnostic category in the DSM.

Diazepam – is a prescription drug first marketed as Valium and is also marketed in Australia as Antenex. It is commonly used for treating anxiety, insomnia, seizures, muscle spasms (such as in cases of tetanus), restless legs syndrome, alcohol withdrawal, benzodiazepine withdrawal and Ménière's disease (a disorder of the inner ear that can affect hearing and balance to a varying degree). It may also be used before certain medical procedures (such as endoscopies) to reduce tension and anxiety. It depresses the central nervous system.

Disorder – a medical condition involving a disturbance to the usual functioning of the mind or body.

Down syndrome – is a common chromosome disorder due to an extra chromosome number 21 (trisomy 21). Down syndrome causes impairment of cognitive ability, a characteristic face, and multiple malformations. The chromosome abnormality affects both the physical and intellectual development of the individual.

DNA – a long linear polymer found in the nucleus of a cell and formed from nucleotides and shaped like a double helix; associated with the transmission of genetic information.

Dyspraxia – refers to difficulty in planning, sequencing, and carrying out unfamiliar actions in a skillful manner. Poor motor planning is the result of dyspraxia.

Early Intervention – refers to special education and related services provided to children under age five that are designed to identify and treat developmental disabilities as early as possible in order to prevent more serious disability, ensure the maximum growth and development of each child, and assist families as they raise a developmentally disabled child.

Equine Therapy – therapeutic horseback riding (also known as equine-assisted activity or adaptive riding) is used to teach riding skills to people with disabilities. Therapeutic riding is beneficial for children and adults who present with any of a wide range of cognitive, physical, and emotional conditions.

Ethnicity – is a group of people whose members identify with each other, through a common heritage, often consisting of a common language, a common culture (often including a shared religion) and/or an ideology that stresses common ancestry or racial, national, tribal, religious, linguistic, or cultural origin or background.

Executive functioning – executive function is the process or processes that enable an individual to set and reach goals by organizing, strategizing, sequencing, and sustaining behaviour to achieve those goals. It helps a person to connect and apply past experience to present action. It is a set of complex cognitive abilities that control and regulate other abilities and behaviour. Executive functions are necessary for goal-directed behaviour. They include the ability to initiate and stop reflexive actions and responses, to monitor and change behaviour as needed, and to plan future behaviour when faced with novel tasks and situations. Executive functioning enables us to anticipate outcomes and adapt to changing situations. The ability to form concepts and think abstractly are often considered components of executive function; a set of abilities required to attain goals efficiently in non-routine situations. (Kodituwakku, 2007).

Expressive Language – the ability to communicate by expressing thoughts using spoken language.

Failure to thrive – is a term used to describe children early in life who do not receive or are unable to take in or retain adequate nutrition to gain weight and grow as expected. Often, children with FASD are initially diagnosed with failure to thrive.

Family – persons who play a significant role in an individual's life and act as his/her support network.

Family support worker – is a case manager who works with people who have developmental disabilities and are living with their families.

Fetal Alcohol Effects (FAE) – was a term formerly used to describe the impairment to a child exposed to alcohol prenatally, however the impairment did not satisfy the criteria for a diagnosis of FAS due to a lack of the characteristic facial features and/or growth delay. The term FAE was not a diagnosis, and is no longer in common use. Many individuals who would have previously fit this category would now be considered to have Neurobehavioural Disorder (or ARND) under the new diagnostic criteria.

Fetal Alcohol Spectrum disorders (FASD) – is an umbrella term describing the range of effects that can occur in an individual whose mother drank alcohol during pregnancy. These effects may include physical, cognitive, sensory, behavioural, and/or learning disabilities with possible lifelong implications. The term FASD is not intended for use as a clinical diagnosis.

Fetal Alcohol Syndrome (FAS) – is the term coined in the United States in 1973 by Dr. Kenneth Jones and Dr. David Smith at the University of Washington to describe individuals with documented prenatal exposure to alcohol and (1) prenatal and postnatal growth retardation, (2) characteristic facial features, and (3) central nervous system problems. Individuals with this diagnosis have all three of the features associated with prenatal alcohol exposure—(1) growth impairment, (2) characteristic facial features, and (3) severe learning and behaviour problems. This is the only fetal alcohol spectrum diagnosis that can be made without a confirmed history of alcohol exposure, because it is unlikely that all three would occur together for any other reason.

Fetal Alcohol Syndrome (FAS) with Confirmed Maternal Alcohol Exposure – is where the diagnostic criteria include: Confirmed prenatal alcohol exposure, the presence of all 3 characteristic facial features (short palpebral fissures, smooth philtrum, thin upper lip), growth deficiency, and evidence of impairment in 3 or more of the following central nervous system (CNS) domains: hard and soft neurologic signs; brain structure; cognition; communication; academic achievement; memory; executive functioning and abstract reasoning; attention deficit/hyperactivity; and adaptive behaviour, social skills and social communication.

FAS without Confirmed Maternal Alcohol Exposure – is when the diagnostic criteria are the same as above, however the presence of prenatal alcohol exposure is unconfirmed. The characteristic facial features of FAS make this the only diagnosis under the FASD umbrella that is possible without confirmed prenatal substance exposure.

Fetal Alcohol Syndrome: Guidelines for Referral and Diagnosis – are guidelines that were published in 2004 by the Centers for Disease Control and Prevention, in collaboration with the National Task Force on Fetal Alcohol Syndrome and Fetal Alcohol Effect in the U.S. They are intended to assist physicians and allied health professionals in the timely identification, referral, and diagnosis of persons with FAS. The guidelines include specific diagnostic criteria in the areas of facial dysmorphia, growth problems, central nervous system abnormalities, and maternal alcohol exposure.

Fetal hypoxia – refers to low levels of oxygen during fetal development, which can cause brain damage. Prenatal alcohol exposure may cause fetal hypoxia.

Fetus – is a developing being, usually from three months after conception until birth for humans. Prior to that time, the developing being is typically referred to as an embryo.

Fine Motor Skills – coordination of small muscle movements which occur (e.g. in the fingers) usually in coordination with the eyes.

Functional Assessment – the measurement of purposeful behaviour in interaction with the environment which is interpreted according to the assessment's intended use. It is the process of appraisal which can be used to measure ability, competence, or performance.

Generalizing Information – is the ability to generalize information; form links and make associations, able to apply a learned rule in a new setting. Many children with FASD have difficulty generalizing information. For example, Jane knows not to run out of the yard at her home, but may not generalize that the same rule applies in her friend's yard.

Genetic disorders – are caused by a disturbance of one gene or several genes or chromosomes. They may be inherited or caused by environmental factors. Genetic disorders may cause various diseases and disorders.

Gross Motor Skills – large muscle and body control and coordination; movements which primarily require the larger muscle groups.

Group home – is a house where two or more youth or developmentally disabled adults individuals live together with a high level of support and an element of supervision.

Hormone imbalance – is when there is too little or too much of a particular hormone in one's body. Hormones are the chemical messengers in the body that travel the bloodstream to the organs and tissues. Even a small imbalance can cause changes in the body.

Hyperkinetic disorders – are characteristic persistent traits of severe and pervasive inattentiveness, over-activity, and impulsiveness, beginning in the first five years of life.

Hypersensitivity – overly responsive to sensory information or input through the mouth (tactile), nose (olfactory), eyes (visual), skin (tactile), balance (vestibular), movement (proprioception).

Hypersensivity to movement – excessive sensations of disorientation, loss of balance, nausea, or headache in response to linear and/or rotary movement. Response may be delayed up to several hours after receiving the input.

Hyposensitivity – under-responsive to sensory information or input through the mouth (tactile), nose (olfactory), eyes (visual), skin (tactile), balance (vestibular), movement (proprioception). Hyposensitivity results in a tendency to crave intense sensations.

Immaturity – not fully grown or developed, a person does not respond to the circumstances or environment in an appropriate manner given their chronological age.

Impulsivity – acts on impulse rather than thought.

Incidence – is the rate at which new events occur in a population.

Inclusion – is an attitude and approach that seeks to ensure that every person, regardless of ability or background, can meaningfully participate in all aspects of life. Inclusion means offering the same opportunities for people with and without disabilities.

Hereditary Disorders – are genetic disorders caused by a genetic or chromosomal abnormality in a parent that is transmitted to a child (e.g., Fragile X syndrome). FASD cannot be inherited.

Intellectual Deficits (Disability) – is a below-average cognitive ability with three characteristics: Intelligent quotient (or I.Q.) is between 70-75 or below, significant limitations in adaptive behaviours, and the onset of the disability occurs before age 18 or year of emancipation.

Intelligence – refers to general mental capability and involves the ability to reason, plan, solve problems, think abstractly, comprehend complex ideas, learn quickly, and learn from experience. The impact of having an intellectual disability varies considerably, just as the range of abilities varies considerably among all people.

Intelligence Quotients (I.Q.) – is a number representing a person's reasoning ability (measured using problem-solving tests) as compared to the statistical norm or average for their chronological age. Generally, a score within 100 is considered Average. There is some debate as to the accuracy of I.Q. testing considering multiple variables, such as English as a second language.

Invisible Disability (sometimes referred to as invisible or hidden disability) – refers to various forms of disability which are not overtly physical. This may include a number of emotional or behavioural concerns, learning disorders, or diagnosed mental health issues which may impair an individual's ability to function at the same level as their peers, while not presenting an observable physical disability.

Learning Disabilities (LD) – are identified difficulties with reading, writing, spelling, computing, or communication. LD affects people's ability to either interpret what they see and hear or to link information from different parts of the brain. These limitations can show up in many ways, as specific difficulties with spoken and written language, coordination, self-control, or attention. Such difficulties extend to schoolwork and can impede learning to read, write, or do math.

Learning Style – the preferred way by which people learn. Common learning styles include: visual (learn by seeing), auditory (learn by hearing) and kinesthetic (learn by doing).

Learning Disorder – refers to a difficulty in learning to read, write, compute, or do school work that cannot be attributed to impaired sight or hearing, or to severe intellectual disability.

Low Birthweight – is a weight below 2,500 grams or 5 pounds, 8 ounces at the time of birth. This standard may need to be revised to reflect variations among different racial and ethnic groups.

Low tone/low endurance – the lack of supportive muscle tone, usually with increased mobility at the joints; the person with low tone has limbs that are floppy, appear to not be attached to the body, and have awkward movement patterns. Lack of muscle tone results in poor ability to sustain a physical activity.

Medical disposition – a tendency either physical or mental towards certain diseases or conditions.

Memory – the ability to compute and to reason. The working memory is the system used for holding and manipulating information while various mental tasks are carried out.

Mental health disorder – is a problem with thinking, mood, behaviour, or a combination of these that meets the criteria set out in the *Diagnostic and Statistical Manual of Disorders IV (1994)*. A mental health problem has a significant impact on a person's daily life, but is not severe enough, or does not last long enough, to meet the criteria for a diagnosis of any disorder.

Math – the ability to compute and to reason.

Microcephaly – is a congenital anomaly of the CNS where the head circumference is more than 3 standard deviations below the mean for age and sex.

Micrognathia – is a relative term describing the small size of the lower jaw. The jaw is too small and can interfere with feeding an infant and may require special nipples in order to feed properly.

Neonatal abstinence syndrome (NAS) – refers to withdrawal symptoms at birth among infants born with a substance such as cocaine, heroin, or alcohol in their bodies at high levels. Symptoms include tremors (trembling), irritability (excessive crying), sleep problems, high-pitched crying, tight muscle tone, hyperactive reflexes, seizures, yawning, stuffy nose and sneezing, poor feeding and suck, vomiting, diarrhea, dehydration, sweating, and fever or unstable temperature.

Neurobehavioural – linking behaviours to brain dysfunction.

Neurobehavioural Disorder – this is a descriptive diagnosis and not an etiological (causal) diagnosis. It is used to describe individuals who have learning and behaviour problems that are less severe and/or less varied than those described as having Static Encephalopathy. It is a major medical finding.

Neurological – having to do with the nerves or the nervous system: the brain, spinal cord and the nerves.

Occupational Therapy – is a therapy or treatment provided by an occupational therapist that helps an individual's developmental or physical skills that will aid in daily living skills such as dressing, eating, and sensory and perceptual-motor integration. It helps decrease physical stress, improve functioning in order to develop skills leading to greater independence in personal, social, academic, and vocational activities.

Oppositional defiant disorder (ODD) – is defined by the Diagnostic and Statistical Manual of Mental Disorders, fourth edition (DSM-IV), as a recurring pattern of negative, hostile, disobedient, and defiant behaviour in a child or adolescent, lasting for at least six months without serious violation of the basic rights of others.

Organic Brain Dysfunction (OBD) – was coined in 1998 at the OBD Triage Institute ©. It refers to brain dysfunction / injury as a result of a teratogenic insult (something that can cause damage to a fetus or embryo in pregnancy.) Non-organic brain injury is postnatal brain injury such as a fall causing brain injury after the infant is born.

Organization – is the act of rearranging parts following one or more rules. Anything is commonly considered organized when it looks like everything has a correct order or placement.

Overall Functioning Capacity – is the level of functioning abilities required in all areas of daily living. Individuals living with FASD typically have variables in different areas of functioning, and may not be on target with their chronological age in some abilities. It is also possible for children with FASD to be advanced in some areas of functioning, while having challenges in other areas.

Palpebral Fissures – are eye openings. The palpebral fissure is measured from the inner canthus (corner) of the eye to the outer canthus of the eye. Short palpebral fissures usually measure below –2 standard deviations for age.

Partial FAS (pFAS) – is a term used to describe a cluster of problems in individuals who are known to have confirmed history of alcohol exposure and have some features of Fetal Alcohol Syndrome. These include some of the characteristic facial abnormalities associated with FAS and evidence of one other component of FAS such as growth deficiency, neurodevelopmental abnormalities, cognitive abnormalities and behaviour that unexplained by family/social history or environment.

Patient-specific Strategies – are plans based on comprehensive information about a person, their medical diagnosis, abilities in learning and sensory integration as well as their interests and goals. The intention is to empower the person towards self-directed goals that build on strengths and aspirations, while supporting their challenges.

Perception – is the meaning the brain gives to sensory input. Sensations are objective; perception is subjective.

Perceptual Reasoning – the ability to solve problems requiring visual perception, organization and reasoning with visually presented, nonverbal material.

Perseveration – is doing the same thing over and over or "get stuck" on a thought or an idea. For example, repeating a request although denied, movement, talking about one topic and not being able to change focus. Individuals that struggle with perseveration may have difficulties with changes in their environment such as a new teacher, new food or routine. They may present as rigid, have difficulty stopping an activity, or transitioning to a new activity.

Philtrum – is the vertical groove between the nose and the middle part of the upper lip.

Physical Therapy – is a health profession concerned with improving a person's physical ability. In a pediatric setting, the physical therapist evaluates a child's orthopedic structure and neuromuscular functions. A physical therapist can also receive special training identical to that received by an occupational therapist to assess and remediate the disorders in sensory processing that influence learning and behaviour.

Placenta – A temporary organ joining the mother and fetus, the placenta transfers oxygen and nutrients from the mother to the fetus, and permits the release of carbon dioxide and waste products from the fetus.

Prenatal Care – involves regular medical care and monitoring during pregnancy. Prenatal care is necessary for healthy pregnancies.

Prenatal exposure to alcohol (PEA) – refers to the exposure of a fetus to alcohol through maternal drinking during pregnancy.

Prevalence of FASD – is how commonly a disease or condition occurs in a population. The prevalence of FASD is estimated to be 10 per 1,000 live births in the U.S. and in Health Canada's Framework for Action on FASD, the incidence is estimated to be nine in 1,000 live births. It is also estimated that the incidence of FAS/FASD in some Aboriginal communities in Canada and the U.S. is higher. Studies have suggested rates from 25 to 200 per 1,000 live births in some isolated communities. Prevalence rates in other countries are not typically known to date, as diagnostic evaluations/clinics for FASD are not yet available world-wide.

Prevention – is the protection of health through personal and communitywide efforts. FASD is 100 percent preventable if women do not drink while pregnant.

Proprioception – refers to the unconscious awareness of sensation from the muscles and joints. Proprioceptive input tells the brain when and how muscles are contracting or stretching, and when and how the joints are bending, extending or being pulled or compressed. This information enables the brain to know where each part of the body is and how it is moving or the "position sense." This sense underlies one's ability to place body parts in a position in space and to evaluate movements such as the ability to judge direction of force and pressure. For example, where and how hard you place and press a stamp on an envelope.

Processing Speed – means the speed or fluency in accurately performing tasks or solving problems. How quickly you are able to think through a new situation, problem-solve, visually scan something, or complete handwriting.

Professional (Clinical) consultation – indicates relevant professional consultation and guidance on issues relating to the effective and appropriate provision of services, such as: maintaining confidentiality; setting boundaries, and working with families with complex issues.

Protective Factors – are things that reduce risk of an adverse outcome, for example a stable home environment, or community support services.

Psychologist – refers to a professional specializing in diagnosing and treating diseases of the brain, emotional disturbance, and behaviour problems. Psychologists can only use talk therapy as treatment; you must see a psychiatrist or other medical doctor to be treated with medication.

Reactive Attachment Disorder – is a rare but serious condition in which infants and young children don't establish healthy bonds with parents or caregivers. A child with reactive attachment disorder is typically neglected, abused or orphaned. Reactive attachment disorder develops because the child's basic needs for comfort, affection and nurturing aren't met and loving, caring attachments with others are never established. This may permanently change the child's growing brain, hurting the ability to establish future relationships. Reactive attachment disorder is a lifelong condition, but with treatment children can develop more stable and healthy relationships with caregivers and others. Safe and proven treatments for reactive attachment disorder include psychological counseling and parent or caregiver education (Mayo Clinic).

Reading: comprehension – the level of understanding of written material.

Receptive language – the ability to understand spoken language.

Remorse – is an emotional expression of personal regret, or sadness. The emotion felt by the individual after he or she has injured someone else in some way. Remorse is associated with feelings of guilt and self-directed resentment.

Risk Factors – situations or things that make a person more likely to engage in a potentially harmful behaviour. For example, being raised in an alcoholic environment would be considered a risk factor in the individual becoming addicted to alcohol.

Romberg Testing (also referred to as Romberg's test) – is a test used by doctors in a neurological examination, and also as a test for drunken driving. The exam is based on the premise that a person requires at least two of the three following senses to maintain balanced while standing: Proprioception (the ability to know one's body in space); Vestibular function (the ability to know one's head position in space); and Vision (which can be used to monitor and adjust for changes in body position).

Secondary Disabilities – were described by Streissguth and Kanter in 1997. They are specific problems that may in the life course of individuals with a diagnosis within FASD. They may be prevented through an enhanced understanding of the disorder, early identification, and appropriate early interventions. Secondary disabilities associated with FASD include disrupted school experiences, trouble with the law, confinement in mental health/substance abuse treatment/criminal justice facilities, inappropriate sexual behaviour, substance abuse disorders, dependent living, and problems with employment.

Self-abusive (harm) – abuse of one's body or health.

Self-centred – totally preoccupied with one's own concerns.

Self-esteem – is an individual's evaluation or judgment of their own worth.

Sensitivity – is the quality or condition of being sensitive or the capacity to respond to stimulation.

Sensory Integration – is how the brain interprets stimuli using information from all of our senses.

Sensory Integration (SID) Dysfunction – is a neurological disorder involving brain processing dysfunction of information received through the senses. Sensory integration dysfunction may be present in motor, learning, social/emotional, speech/language or attention disorders.

Sequencing – is to put things in, or experience the beginning, middle and end of an event in the correct order.

Sexualized Behaviour – demonstrating advanced knowledge of sexual behaviour which is not considered age appropriate.

Shared Care or Respite Care – is care for an individual by a person other than the usual caregiver as a form of rest or break for the caregiver(s). Shared care may be with a family member, friend or approved agency where the child, youth or adult may be tended to in or out of the home.

Spectrum – a range of values or ideas.

Speech/Language Therapy – is therapy or treatment by a Speech Pathologist or Therapist to improve and correct speech, language, and/or communication problems.

Supported Employment – is described as ongoing support provided by an agency with expertise in working with Persons with Disabilities. Individualized program plans are developed for people that require intensive on-going assistance to obtain and maintain employment in the community. Supported employment services may provide a one-on-one staff to help guide the individual with finding and securing employment, and work duties. Support is individualized and may include any combination of the following services: person-centered employment planning, abilities/interests assessment, transportation and job searches, negotiation with prospective employers, training and/or coaching/mentoring.

Static Encephalopathy – refers to brain injury that is not progressive, or that will not worsen. It is permanent brain injury cannot be rehabilitated. This diagnosis refers to individuals who have structural, neurological and/or significant functional abnormalities to their brain (central nervous system).

Strengths-based approach – an approach that promotes the individual's strengths, abilities, and interests in order to promote success in all areas of functioning including home, academic, vocational, employment, social/personal, recreational, and community environments.

Supported Independent Living (SIL) – provides supports to people who do not require 24-hour a day, seven days a week staffing. Individuals are mentored in learning to cook, clean, budget their monies, and participate in social recreational activities with limited staff support. Agencies that provide SIL placements are often government funded.

Swaddling – is the process of wrapping a baby tightly in a blanket. In the case of infants prenatally exposed to alcohol and/or drugs, it is intended to keep babies from being disturbed by their own startle reflex, and provides warmth and security. Swaddling is known to be effective in calming infants with Neonatal Abstinence Syndrome (withdrawal).

Syndrome – a set of symptoms occurring together.

Tactile – refers to information taken into the body through the sense of touch (skin).

Tactile defensiveness – individuals who have tactile defensiveness are sensitive to touch sensations and can be easily overwhelmed or fearful of ordinary daily experiences and activities. It is associated with distractibility, restlessness, and often translates to what appears to be intentionally defiant behaviour problems.

Teratogen – is defined as any agent or factor which causes abnormalities of development in an embryo or fetus. This includes alcohol, some drugs, cigarette smoke, DNA mutations or various syndromes, virus.

The FASD 4-Digit Diagnostic Code – is an evaluation tool for diagnosis of FASD and was developed by the Fetal Alcohol Syndrome (FAS) Diagnostic and Prevention Network at the University of Washington in response to the need to standardize criteria for the diagnosis of fetal alcohol spectrum disorders. The four digits of the diagnostic system consider the extent to which the individual presents with the four key diagnostic features of FAS or related disorders: growth retardation, facial features, brain dysfunction, and prenatal alcohol exposure. An individual receives a rank on each of these scales and a diagnostic code based on the pattern of the four rankings. Twelve different 4-digit diagnostic code patterns may indicate an FAS diagnosis. Various other patterns may indicate atypical FAS, static encephalopathy, neurobehavioral disorder, or no detected cognitive or physical findings. The 4-Digit Diagnostic Code has shown excellent consistency and reliability.

The Diagnostic and Statistical Manual of Mental Disorders (DSM-IV) – refers to the book that is used by mental health professionals to diagnose mental health disorders. For each disorder, the DSM-IV lists specific criteria for making a diagnosis.

Understanding Social Rules – implies understanding the rules and concepts required for positive social interactions. This could include understanding matter-of-fact speech, social rules of manners and etiquette, gestures, inferences, abstractions, sayings or figure of speech, innuendo.

Withdrawal – is a group of symptoms that may occur from suddenly stopping the use of an addictive substance such as alcohol and/or drugs after chronic or prolonged use. Newborn babies can experience withdrawal from substances in cases where the mother consumed alcohol and/or drugs in her pregnancy.

Written Expression – the ability to communicate in writing, independent of spelling ability. This may include physical reproduction of letters and words, and the organization of thoughts and ideas in written compositions.

Verbal Comprehension – the ability to reason with words and express acquired knowledge.

Vestibular System – describes the sensory system that responds to changes in head and body movement through space, and coordinates movements of the eyes, head, and body. The receptor site of the vestibular system is in the inner ear and is connected to receptors of auditory (hearing) and visual senses. Gravitational Insecurity is an extreme fear that causes anxiety that one will fall when one's head position changes. For example, children who refuse to have their hair washed in a sink may react in the extreme.

Visual-spatial Organization – describes the process that we use to perceive and interpret what the eyes see. Information is taken in through the eyes, and sent to the brain and then organized resulting in the ability to accurately interpret depth perception, directionality, form constancy, position in space, spatial awareness (the distance between you and objects), visual discrimination, visual figure-ground (distance between objects). It also includes vertical/horizontal/diagonal perception and plane integration. These abilities are necessary for processing mathematical problems.

Wechsler Intelligence Scales – are a series of standardized tests used to evaluate cognitive abilities and intellectual abilities in children and adults.

Footnotes

[1] "FASD Diagnostic Clinic." http://depts.washington.edu/fasdpn/ retrieved July 1, 2011

[2] "Sperm Count Risk Factors." Mayo Clinic. http://www.mayoclinic.com/health/low-sperm-count/DS01049/DSECTION=risk-factors Retrieved June 22, 2011.

[3] "Alcohol intake and cigarette smoking: impact of two major lifestyle factors on male fertility." (2010). Gaur DS, Talekar MS, Pathak VP . Indian J Pathol Microbiol. 2010 Jan-Mar; 53(1):35-40 Department of Pathology, Himalayan Institute of Medical Sciences, Jolly Grant, Dehradun 248 140, Uttarakhand, India.

[4] "Drinking alcohol during pregnancy." http://www,marchofdimes.com/alcohol_indepth.html Retrieved October 6, 2011

[5] "Smith's Recognizable Patterns of Human Malformations." Revised edition 1982. Smith, David W. WB Saunders Company, Harcourt Brace Jovanovich, Inc. Philadelphia, P.A, page 491-499.

[6] "Drugs in Pregnancy." Motherisk . http://www.motherisk.org/women/index.jsp Adapted by Liz Lawryk OBD Triage Institute 2011.

[7] "Prenatal Alcohol and Drug Exposures in Adoption.". (2005). J Davies, J Bledsoe Paediatric Clinics of North America, Volume 52, Issue 5, Page 1383.

[8] "Drugs in Pregnancy.".Motherisk: http://www.motherisk.org/women/drugs.jsp Retrieved and Adapted on July 14, 2010: Lawryk, Liz OBD Triage Institute 2011.

[9] "The **OBD** Triage Instrument: A Screening Instrument for use in the Medical Evaluation of Teratogenic Effects on Embryonic Development." (2011 R.) Lawryk, L. © OBD Triage Institute 2010.

[10] "Drugs in Pregnancy.".Motherisk: http://www.motherisk.org/women/drugs.jsp Retrieved and Adapted on July 14, 2010: Lawryk, L. OBD Triage Institute 2011.

[11] "Brain Cell Development." 2010 Brain Health and Puzzles http://scholar.google.ca/scholar?q=b rain+and+health+puzzle&hl=en&as_sdt=0&as_vis=1&oi=scholart. Retrieved February 14, 2011.

[12] "Human Biology and Health." (1993). Anthea; Maton, Hopkins, Jean, McLaughlin, Charles William, Johnson, Susan, Quon, Maryanna, Warner, David, LaHart, Jill D. Wright. Englewood Cliffs, New Jersey, USA: Prentice Hall. pp. 132–144

[13] "Definition of fetus." Wikipedia Found in: Klossner, N. Jayne Introductory Maternity Nursing (2005): "The fetal stage is from the beginning of the 9th week after fertilization and continues until birth", The American Pregnancy Association. http://en.wikipedia.org/wiki/ Fetus. Retrieved August 1, 2011.

[14] "Definitions and Indicators in Family Planning. Maternal & Child Health and Reproductive Health." By European Regional Office, World Health Organization. Revised March 1999 & January 2001. In turn citing: WHO Geneva, WHA20.19, WHA43.27, Article 23 in http:// en.wikipedia.org/wiki/Pregnancy#Prenatal_period Retrieved March 16, 2011.

[15] "Neonatal Abstinence Syndrome." http://www.nlm.nih.gov/medlineplus/ency/article/007313. htm. Retrieved October 6, 2011.

[16] "Neonatal Abstinence Syndrome"; http://www.nlm.nih.gov/medlineplus/ency/article/007313. htm. Retrieved October 6, 2011

[17] "Encyclopaedia of Drugs, Alcohol and Addictive Behaviour." http://www.enotes.com/drugs-alcohol-encyclopedia/addicted-babies Retrieved October 5, 2011.

[18] "Neonatal abstinence syndrome: assessment and pharmacotherapy." Finnegan LP . In: Nelson N, editor. Current therapy in neonatal-perinatal medicine. 2 ed. Ontario: BC Decker; 1990.

[19] "Definition of Genetics." http://www.medterms.com/script/main/art.asp?articlekey=15390. Retrieved, October 30, 2011.

[20] "FAS DPN FASD 4-Digit Code." (2004). Astley, S. http://depts.washington.edu/fasdpn/htmls/4-digit-code.htm Retrieved Aug.1, 2009.

[21] "FAS Facial Features." Astley, S. Used with Permission. http://depts.washington.edu/fasdpn/htmls/fas-face.htm Retrieved August 3, 2009.

[22] "FAS Facial Features Photo." Astley, S. Used with Permission.Copyright 2011.

[23] "FAS Facial Features." Astley, S. http://depts.washington.edu/fasdpn/htmls/fas-face.htm Retrieved August 3, 2009.

[24] "FAS Facial Features Photographs." Astley, S. University of Washington, Seattle, Washington. Used with Permission.

[25] "4-Digit Diagnostic Code." Clarren S., Astley S. University of Washington - Adapted on July 14, 2010: Lawryk, L. OBD Triage Institute 2011.

[26] "Teratogen." Tabers Cyclopedic Medical Dictionary. Davis F.A Edition 19. Page 2152.

[27] "Megaloblastic anemia." Antony A C. In: Hoffman R, Benz EJ, Shattil SS, et al., eds. Hematology: Basic Principles and Practice. 5th ed. Philadelphia, Pa: Elsevier Churchill Livingstone; 2008: chap 39.

[28] "FAS Facial Features Photo." Astley, S. University of Washington. Used with Permission. Copyright 2011.

[29] "The Out-Of-Sync Child: Recognizing and Coping With Sensory Processing Disorder." (2005). Revised Edition . Stock-Kranowitz, C. Perigee. Used with permission.

[30] "The Out-Of-Sync Child: Recognizing and Coping With Sensory Processing Disorder."(2005). Revised Edition . Stock-Kranowitz, C. Perigee. Used with permission.

[31] "Sexual imprinting." http://en.wikipedia.org/wiki/Imprinting_(psychology) Retrieved July 11, 2011.

[32] Judy R. 2010.

[33] "Exceptional Children: An Introduction to Special Education." (2005). Heward, William. 8th Edition Prentice Hall Publisher. http://en.wikipedia.org/wiki/Adaptive_behaviour#cite_note-Heward-0. Retrieved June 26, 2011.

[34] "Wechsler Intelligence Scales for Children - Revised (WISC-IV)." (2008). Weschler, D. San Antonio, Texas, U.S.A. The Psychological Corporation. Harcourt Brace and Company.

[35] "FAS Diagnostic & Prevention Network." (NPIF doc 1/1/99). Clarren, 1982; Harvard Medical School, 1990. Adapted from: University of Washington.

[36] Adapted by Lawryk, L. OBD Triage Institute. " Educational Implications." from: by Susan Doctor. In press.

[37] "Understanding the occurrence of secondary disabilities in clients with fetal alcohol syndrome (FAS) and fetal alcohol effects (FAE). "(1996). Final report to the Centers for Disease Control and Prevention. Streissguth A, Barr H, Kogan J & Bookstein F. Seattle: University of Washington School of Medicine, 1996.

[38] "Understanding the occurrence of secondary disabilities in clients with fetal alcohol syndrome (FAS) and fetal alcohol effects (FAE)." (1996). Final report to the Centers for Disease Control and Prevention. Streissguth A, Barr H, Kogan J & Bookstein F. Seattle: University of Washington School of Medicine, 1996.

[39] "What Advocates Have Said." Wolfensberger, Wolf. Published in Citizen Advocacy Forum, Vol. 11, No. 2, November 2001, pp. 4-27.

[40] "What Advocates Have Said." Wolfensberger, Wolf. Published in Citizen Advocacy Forum, Vol. 11, No. 2, November 2001, pp. 4-27.

[41] "UNODC Executive Director visits drug treatment centre in Tehran." United Nations Office on Drugs and Crime July 20, 2011. http://www.unodc.org/unodc/en/frontpage/2011/July/unodc-executive-director-visits-drug-treatment-centre-in-tehran.html?ref=fs1 Retrieved July 23, 2011.

[42] "Prenatal Alcohol and Drug Exposures in Adoption." J Davies, J Bledsoe. Paediatric Clinics of North America, Volume 52, Issue 5, Page 1371.

[43] "Maternal-substance use and subsequent sudden infant death syndrome (SIDS) in offspring." (1991). Kandall SR, Gaines J .Mar-Apr; 13(2): 235-40. Neonatology and Chemical Dependency Institute, Beth Israel Medical Center, New York, NY 10003

[44] "New research shows overheating newborns can increase the risk of SIDS." By Marta Cyperling Posted June 2, 2008. Dr. Shabih Hasan, professor in the Department of Paediatrics at the University of Calgary Faculty of Medicine *American Journal of Respiratory and Critical Care Medicine. June 2011.* http://medicine.ucalgary.ca/about/sids Retrieved July 17, 2011.

[45] "The Best I can be: Living with Fetal Alcohol Syndrome and Effects." Kulp, Jodee and Liz. Used with permission, pp 80.

[46] The Four Agreements © 1997, don Miguel Ruiz. Reprinted by permission of Amber-Allen Publishing, Inc. P.O. Box 6657, San Rafael, CA 94903. All rights reserved."

[47] "FAS Diagnostic and Prevention Network FASD 4-Digit Diagnostic Code." http://depts.washington.edu/fasdpn/htmls/4-digit-code.htm Retrieved October 5, 2011.

[48] "DIAGNOSING THE FULL SPECTRUM OF FETAL ALCOHOL EXPOSED INDIVIDUALS: INTRODUCING THE 4-DIGIT DIAGNOSTIC CODE." Susan J. Astley, Ph.D.1,2 and Sterling K. Clarren, M.D.2 Alcohol & Alcoholism Vol. 35, No. 4, pp. 400-410, 2000. © 2000 Medical Council on Alcoholism. Department of Epidemiology, School of Public Health and Community Medicine and 2Department of Pediatrics, School of Medicine, University of Washington, Seattle, Washington, USA. (Received 18 November 1999; in revised form 24 March 2000; accepted 30 March 2000.)

[49] Source: Family Helper, www.familyhelper.net. Used with permission – Robin Hillborn © Adoption Helper http://www.familyhelper.net/news/index.html

References

A

"A brief introduction to Social Role Valorization: A high-order concept for addressing the plight of societally devalued people, and for structuring human services." (1998). Wolfensberger, W. (3rd ed.). Syracuse, NY: Training Institute for Human Service Planning, Leadership and Change Agentry (Syracuse University).

"A child with fetal alcohol syndrome."(2000). Clarren, S. K., Carmichael Olson, H., Clarren, S. G. B., & Astley, S. J. *In M. J. Guralnick (Ed.), Interdisciplinary clinical assessment of young children with developmental disabilities* (pp. 307–326)

"A Parents Guide to Understanding Sensory Integration," Published by Sensory Integration International, 1402 Cravens Ave. Torrance, CA 90501-2701 (1991)

"A Review of the Neurobehavioural Deficits in children with fetal alcohol syndrome or prenatal exposure to alcohol." (1998). Mattson, S. N., & Riley, E. P. (*Alcoholism: Clinical and Experimental Research*, 22, 279–294)

"About Cerebral Palsy." www.about-cerebral-palsy.org Retrieved October 23, 2011.

"Abstract concepts." http://medical-dictionary.thefreedictionary.com Abstract+concept Retrieved August 12, 2011.

"Adoption State Statutes Series Statutes-at-a-Glance: Collection of Family Information About Adopted Persons, Birth Parents, and Adoptive Parents." (2003). *U.S. Department of Health and Human Services. Administration for Children and Families. National Adoption Information Clearinghouse.* http://naic.acf.hhs.gov/general/legal/statutes/collection.pdf

"Adopting and fostering children with fetal alcohol spectrum disorders." (2007). SAMHSA (Substance Abuse and Mental Health Services Administration).DHHS Publication No. (SMA) 07–4254. (Printed 2007)

"Alcohol & Alcoholism". (2000). Vol. 35, No. 4, pp. 400-410,. © 2000 Medical Council on Alcoholism.

"Alcohol, tobacco, and other drugs may harm the unborn." (1990). Cook, P. Shannon, Petersen, R. C.,Moore, D.T. DHHS Publication no. (ADM)90-1711. Rockville, MD: U.S. Department of Health and Human Services.

"Alcohol intake and cigarette smoking: impact of two major lifestyle factors on male fertility." (2010). *Department of Pathology, Himalayan Institute of Medical Sciences*, Jolly Grant, Dehradun 248 140, Uttarakhand, India. Gaur DS, Talekar MS, Pathak VP . Indian J Pathol Microbiol. (Retrieved July 27, 2011 2010 Jan-Mar; 53 (1):35-40)

"Alcohol-Related Birth Defects, The Past, Present and Future." Kenneth R. Warren, Ph. D., and Laurie L. Foudin, Ph. D. *National Institute on Alcohol Abuse and Alcoholism.* http://pubs.niaaa.nih.gov/publications/arh25-3/153-158.htm (Retrieved 2011-05-29)

"Amphetamine." http://en.wikipedia.org/wiki/Amphetamine Retrieved October 24, 2011.

"An Ecological model of Sensory Modulation: Performance of children with fragile X syndrome, autistic disorder, attention-deficit/hyperactivity disorder, and sensory modulation." (2001). Miller, L. J., Reisman, J. E., McIntosh, D. N., & Simon J. *The American Journal of Occupational Therapy 273 dysfunction.*

"An update on incidence of FAS: FAS is not an equal opportunity birth defect." (1995). ABEL, E. L.(*Neurotoxicology and Teratology* 17(4) : 437 443.

"Apgar score." http://en.wikipedia.org/wiki/Apgar_score. Retrieved October 23, 2011.

"Application of the fetal alcohol syndrome facial photographic screening tool in a foster care population." (2002). Astley SJ; Stachowiak J; Clarren SK; Clausen C. (Journal of Pediatrics 141(5): pp 712-717

"Applying Principles of Neurodevelopment to Clinical Work with Maltreated and Traumatized Children." (2006). Perry, B.D. In: Working with Traumatized Youth in Child Welfare. Copyright 2006. Guilford Press. New York, N.Y.

B

"Barbiturates." http://en.wikipedia.org/wiki/Barbiturate Retrieved August 23, 2011.

"Behavioural and psychosocial profiles of alcohol-exposed children."(1999) 1999). Roebuck, T. M., Mattson, S. N., & Riley, E. P. (*Alcoholism: Clinical and Experimental Research*, 23, pp 1070–1076.

"Benefits to Students with Down syndromein the Inclusion Classroom: K-3". (2004). Bosworth, Debra L. http://web.archive.org/web/20080420100218/ http://www.altonweb.com/cs/downsyndrome/index.htm?page=ndssincl.html. Retrieved August 23, 2011.

"Birth Control Pills in Pregnancy." (2010). Harms R.W. Mayo Clinic, Rochester, Minn. http://www.mayoclinic.com/health/birth-control-pills/ AN01662 Retrieved September 2, 2011.

C

"Caffeine and alcohol as risk factors for sudden infant death syndrome." (1999). B Alm, G Wennergren, G Norvenius, R Skjærven, N Øyen, K Helweg-Larsen, H Lagercrantz, L M Irgens on behalf of the Nordic Epidemiological SIDS Study. *Arch Dis Child* 1999; pp 81:107-111 doi:10.1136/adc.81.2.107.

"Care of Babies Experiencing Withdrawal Symptoms." http://www. northdevonhealth.nhs.uk/patientinformation/obstetrics/babies_experiencing_ withdrawal_symptoms.htm (Retrieved 2011-05-29) Refer Appendix C.

"Centre for Addiction and Mental Health Building the Path to HomeLinks to sustainable housing for people with dual diagnosis." http://www.camh. net/path_home/glossary.html

"Children With Prenatal Alcohol and/or Other Drug Exposure: Weighing the Risks of Adoption."(1995). Edelstein, S.Washington, DC: CWLA Press.

"Children with fetal alcohol spectrum disorders: A descriptive profile of adaptive function." (2008). Jirikowic, T. L., Kartin, D., & Olson, H. C. (in press). *Canadian Journal of Occupational Therapy.*

"Children With Fetal Alcohol Spectrum Disorders: Problem Behaviours and Sensory Processing."(2008). Franklin, Laureen, Deitz, Jean, Jirikowic, Tracey, and Astley, Susan. *American Journal of Occupational Therapy May/June 2008 vol. 62 no. 3 265-273* http://ajot.aotapress.net/content/62/3/265.full. pdf+html Retrieved June 16, 2011.

"Citizen Advocacy And Protective Services For The Impaired And Handicapped." (1973). Wolfensberger, W., & Zauha, H.Toronto: National Institute on Mental Retardation.

"Cognitive Functions." (2007). Kodituwakku, P. http://findarticles.com/p/ articles/mi_hb4384/is_8_42/ai_n29459617/ Retrieved October 13, 2011.

"Combining Neuro-developmental and Sensory Integrative Principles: An Approach to Pediatric Therapy."(1995). Blanche, Erna I., M.A., OTR, Botticelli, M.S., PT, Hallway, Mary K., OTR. Tucson: Therapy Skill Builders.

"Community Partnerships, Inc. Glossary". http://www. communitypartnerships.org/resources/glossary Retrieved October 1, 2011.

"Consequence." Collins English Dictionary - Complete and Unabridged © HarperCollins Publishers 1991, 1994, 1998, 2000, 2003 http://www. thefreedictionary.com/consequence. Retrieved October 23, 2011.

"Comparison of Sensory Profile scores of young children with and without autism spectrum disorders." (2001). Watling, R., Deitz, J., & White, O. (*American Journal of Occupational Therapy*, 55, 416–423.

"Comparison of the adaptive functioning of children prenatally exposed to alcohol to a nonexposed clinical sample." (2001). Whaley, S. E., O'Connor, M. J., & Gunderson B. (*Alcoholism:Clinical and Experimental Research*, 25, pp 1018-1025.

"Cost of fetal alcohol spectrum disorders." (2004). Lupton, C., Burd, L., Harwood R. (*Am J Med Genet* 127C(676): 42-50.

D

"Definitions of Sensory Terms." Whitney. R. (2008). http://www.spdbayarea. org/definition_of_sensory_terms.htm Retrieved, October 24, 2011.

"De-Medicalizing Sleep: A Trans-Disciplinary & Trans-Cultural Team approach to Sleep in Children & Adolescents with FASD." (2004). Ipsiroglu, O.S., Garden, J., James, J.E., Kuttner, L., Looke, C. Lucyshyn, J., and Owens, J.A. (4th International Conference on Fetal Alcohol Spectrum Disorder. Vancouver, B.C. 2011-03-04)

"Diagnosing the full spectrum of Fetal Alcohol exposed individuals: Introducing the 4-Digit diagnostic code". (2000). Astley, Susan J. Ph.D(1,2), and Clarren, Sterling, K. M.D (2).

1. Department of Epidemiology, School of Public Health and Community Medicine.

2. Department of Pediatrics, School of Medicine, University of Washington, Seattle, Washington, USA.

"Diagnosing the full spectrum of Fetal Alcohol exposed individuals: Introducing the 4-digitdiagnostic code." (2000). Astley, S. J., & Clarren, S. K. *Alcohol and Alcoholism*, pp 34, 400-410.

"Diagnostic guide for Fetal Alcohol Syndrome and related conditions: The 4-digit diagnostic code." (1997). Astley, S. J., & Clarren, S. K. *Seattle: University of Washington Publication Services.*

"Diagnostic guide for Fetal Alcohol Spectrum Disorders:The 4-digit diagnostic code." (2004). (3rd ed.) Astley, S. J. *Seattle: University of Washington Publication Services.* Used with permission.

"Diazepam." http://en.wikipedia.org/wiki/ Diazepam Retrieved October 24, 2011.

"Disposition". http://www.mondofacto.com/facts/dictionary?query=disposition &action=look+it+up Retrieved October 14, 2011.

"DNA." http://dictionary.kids.net.au/word/DNA Retrieved September 5, 2011.

"Drinking alcohol during pregnancy." http://www.marchofdimes.com/ alcohol_indepth.html Retrieved October 6, 2011.

"Drugs, alcohol, pregnancy and parenting." (1988). Chasnoff, I. J. (Ed.). Boston: Kluwer Academic Publishers.

"Drug-addicted Mothers Need Treatment, Not Punishment." (2000). Lester, B.. *Alcoholism & Drug Abuse Weekly*, 12, 5

E

"Educational Implications." (1997). Doctor, Susan.

"Effects of alcohol and cigarette consumption on human seminal quality. Fertility and Sterility." (2004). Martini, A.C. pp; 82:374.

"Effects of prenatal exposure to alcohol across the lifespan." (1996). Connor, P. D., & Streissguth, A. P. *Alcohol Health and Research World*, pp 20, 170-174.

"Effects of prenatal alcohol exposure at school age: II. Attention and behaviour."(1991). Brown, R.T., Coles, C. D., Smith, I. E., Platzman, K.A., Silverstein, J., Erickson, S., et al. (*Neurotoxicology and Teratology*, pp 13, 369-376.

"Effects of Prenatal Drug Exposures." Koren, Gideon. http://www. motherisk.org/women/index.jsp (Retrieved July 23, 2010)

"Erasing a Hurtful Label From the Books." (2010). Ansberry, C New York: Wall Street Journal. "Decades-long quest by disabilities advocates finally persuades state, federal governments to end official use of 'retarded." http://online.wsj.com/article/SB10001424052748704865104575588273153838564.html Retrieved August 28, 2011.

"Estimating the prevalence of fetal alcohol syndrome: A summary."(2001). May, P.A., and Gossage, J.P. (*Alcohol Research & Health* 25(3): pp 159-167.

"Ethnicity, Language, and Power from a Psycholinguistic Perspective." (1982). Seidner, S. pp. 2-3.

"Executive functioning in children with heavy prenatal alcohol exposure." (1999). Mattson, S. N., Goodman, A. M., Caine, C. D., Delis, D. C., & Riley, E. P. (*Alcoholism: Clinical and Experimental Research*, 23, 1808-1815.

"Exceptional Children: An Introduction to Special Education." (2005). Heward, William. 8th Edition Prentice Hall Publisher. http://en.wikipedia.org/wiki/Adaptive_behaviour#cite_note-Heward-0. Retrieved June 26, 2011.

F

"FASD Diagnostic Clinic." http://depts.washington.edu/fasdpn/ Retrieved July 1, 2011.

"FAS Diagnostic and Prevention Network FASD 4-Digit Diagnostic Code." (2004). http://depts.washington.edu/fasdpn/htmls/4-digit-code.htm Retrieved October 5, 2011.

"FASD Resource Toolkit." Northern Family Health Society http://www.nfhs-g.org/media/FASD_Resource_Toolkit_second_edition.pdf Retrieved October 20, 2011.

"Facts About Down Syndrome." National Down syndromeCongress http://www.ndsccenter.org/resources/package3.php Retrieved June 29, 2011.

"Fetal alcohol exposure and attention: Beyond ADHD." (2001). Coles, C. D.(Alcohol Research and Health, pp. 25, 199-203.

"Fetal Alcohol Syndrome." (2010). Morbeck D.E. Mayo Clinic. Rochester, Minn.http://www.mayoclinic.com/health/fetal-alcohol-syndrome/DS00184/DSECTION=symptoms Retrieved November 11, 2010.

"Fetal alcohol syndrome: Guidelines for referral and diagnosis." (2004). Bertrand, J., Floyd, R. L., Weber, M. K., O'Connor, M., Riley, E. P., Johnson, K. A., et al. Atlanta: Centers for Disease Control and Prevention.

"Fetal alcohol syndrome- Position Statement." Fetal Alcohol Syndrome. (2002). Pediatric Child Health 2002; 7(3): 161-174) (2002-01-11).

"Fetal Alcohol Syndrome Tutor TM Medical Training Software CD-ROM, March of Dimes". (1999). Astley, S.J., Clarren, S.K., Gratzer, M., Orkand, A. and Astion,M.

"Fetal Alcohol Syndrome". (1978). Clarren, S.K, and Smith, D.W. (New England Journal of Medicine 298(19) : 1063 1067.

"Fetal, infant, and child mortality in a context of alcohol use." (2004). Burd, Larry, and Wilson, Harry. http://onlinelibrary.wiley.com/ doi/10.1002/ajmg.c.30016/full Retrieved June 17, (Article first published online: 8 APR 2004.DOI: 10.1002/ajmg.c.30016. Copyright © 2004 Wiley-Liss, Inc. 2011.)

"Finding Perspective … Raising Successful Children Affected by Fetal Alcohol Spectrum Disorder. A Parent's Guide to Creating Prevention Strategies and Intervention Techniques." (2005). Lawryk, L. © **OBD** Triage Institute Publisher.

G

"Genetic influences on craniofacial outcome in an avian model of prenatal alcohol exposure." (2001). Su, B, Debelak, K.A, Tessmer, L.L, Cartrwright, M.M, and Smith, S.M. (*Alcoholism: Clinical and Experimental Research* 25(1) : 60 69.

"Glossary of FASD Terms." - Asante Centre. http://www.asantecentre.org/ glossary.html

"Glossary of FASD terms." The Substance Abuse and Mental Health Services Administration http://fascenter.samhsa.gov/educationtraining/ courses/fasdthecourse/misc/glossary.cfm Retrieved October 12, 2011.

"Glossary of Sensory Integration Terms." University of Alberta Education. http://www.uab.edu/shrpot/SenMotor7_22_04/GLOSSARY_OF_SENSORY_INTEGRA.H Retrieved October 24, 2011.

H

"Healthy sperm: Improving your fertility. What's off-limits?" (2011). Mayo Foundation for Medical Education and Research (MFMER). All rights reserved. *"Mayo," "Mayo Clinic," "MayoClinic.com," "Embody Health," "Enhance your life," and the triple-shield Mayo Clinic logo are trademarks of Mayo Foundation for Medical Education and Research).* Retrieved August 30, 2011.

"Human Biology and Health". (1993). Maton, Anthea; Jean Hopkins, Charles William McLaughlin, Susan Johnson, Maryanna Quon Warner, David LaHart, Jill D. Wright. Englewood Cliffs, New Jersey, USA: Prentice Hall. pp. 132-144.

http://www.mayoclinic.com/health/fertility/MC00023/NSECTIONGROUP=2 Retrieved July 27, 2010.

http://www.medicinenet.com/down_syndrome/page5.htm Retrieved June 30, 2011 pg. 3?

http://www.medicinenet.com/down_syndrome/page5.htm *Alcohol & Alcoholism* Vol. 35, No. 4, pp. 3; 400-410, 2000. (Retrieved 2011-06-30)

http://scholar.google.ca/scholar?q=brain+and+health+puzzle&hl=en&as_sdt=0&as_vis=1&oi=scholart Retrieved May 10, 2011.

http://web.archive.org/web/20080420100218/http://www.altonweb.com/cs/downsyndrome/index.htm?page=ndssincl.html. Retrieved 2006-05-12. Retrieved from Wikipedica on June 30, 2011.

http://www.yourdictionary.com/grammar-rules/abstract-nouns.html,

I

"Imprinting." http://en.wikipedia.org/wiki/Imprinting_(psychology) Retrieved 2011-07-11.

"Inclusion: Educating Students with Down syndromewith Their Non-Disabled Peers". (2008). Armstrong, SE. Archived from the original on 2008-04-20. (Retrieved from Wikipedica on June 30, 2011)

"Infections that can affect pregnancy." (2009). http://www.babycenter.com/0_infections-that-can-affect-pregnancy_9223.bc Retrieved July 24, 2011.

"Intellectual disability." http://en.wikipedia.org/wiki/Intellectual_disability Retrieved July 23, 2011.

L

"Langman's Medical Embryology." Sadler, T.W. (2006). Tenth Edition. Copyright 2010. Lippencott, Williams and Wilkens. Baltimore, Maryland, U.S.A.

"Letters to Our Children, Letters from Our Children: Living with Fetal Alcohol Syndrome and Related Effects." (2000). Badry, D., Lawryk, L. Editors. © Association of Community Living Publishers.

M

"Megaloblastic anemia." Antony AC. (2008) *In: Hoffman R, Benz EJ, Shattil SS, et al., eds.* Hematology: Basic Principles and Practice. 5th ed. (Philadelphia, Pa: Elsevier Churchill Livingstone; chapter 39.)

"Maternal substance use and subsequent sudden infant death syndrome (SIDS) in offspring." (1991). Kandall, SR, Gaines, J. Neonatology and Chemical Dependency Institute, Beth Israel Medical Center, New York, NY.

N

"Neonatal abstinence syndrome." (2010). Ashraf H Hamdan, MD, MBBCh, MSc, MRCP; Chief Editor: Ted Rosenkrantz, MD http://emedicine.medscape.com/article/978763-overview Retrieved October 6, 2011.

"Neonatal diagnosis of Fetal Alcohol Syndrome: Not necessarily a hopeless prognosis." (1995) Ernhart, C.B., Greene, T., Sokol, R.J., Martier, S., Boyd, T.A. and Ager, J. *Alcoholism: Clinical and Experimental Research* 19(6), 1550-7.

"Neurological." http://www.medterms.com/script/main/art.asp?articlekey=16313 Retrieved October 20, 2011.

O

"Optimizing natural fertility in couples planning pregnancy." (2011). Hornstein, MD, et al. http://www.uptodate.com/home/index.html. Retrieved September 5, 2011.

"Overlapping Behavioural Characteristics & Related Mental Health Diagnoses in Children." (2006.) Bruer-Thompson, Cathy. (cathy.bruer-thompson@co.hennepin.mn.us Chart used with permission.

P

"Parent ratings of behaviour in children with heavy prenatal alcohol exposure and I.Q. matched controls." (2000). Mattson, S. N., & Riley, E. P. (*Alcoholism: Clinical and Experimental Research*, 24, 226-231.

"Paths to Inclusion. Including all kids." www.Includingallkids.org Retrieved October 20, 2011.

"Placenta". http://www.medterms.com/script/main/art.asp?articlekey=4918 Retrieved October 22, 2011.

"Pregnancy and Thyroid Disease." National Endrocrine and Metobolic Diseases Information Services. http://endocrine.niddk.nih.gov/pubs/pregnancy/ Retrieved October 5, 2011.

"Prenatal Alcohol and Drug Exposures in Adoption." Davies, J, and Bledsoe, J. (2005). (*Pediatric Clinics of North America*, Volume 52, Issue 5, Pages 1369-1393 Page 1371) Copyright © Elsevier

"Prenatal Cigarette, Cocaine Exposure Tied to Language Problems." (2000). JOHNSON, KATE. OB GYN News, 35, 13.

"Prevalence of FASD." Public Health Agency of Canada http://www.phac-aspc.gc.ca/publicat/fasd-ru-ectaf-pr-06/1-eng.php Retrieved July 12, 2011.

"Protective Factor." (2008). Tull, M. About.com Guide. http://ptsd.about.com/od/glossary/g/Protective.htm Retrieved August 13, 2010.

"Provincial Outreach Program for Fetal Alcohol Spectrum Disorder." Glossary. British Columbia, Canada. http://www.fasdoutreach.ca/glossary Retrieved October 23, 2011.

"Psychologist." http://www.medterms.com/script/main/art.asp?articlekey=5109 Retrieved October 20, 2011.

"Psychology." http://psychology.about.com/od/cindex/g/def_cns.htm Retrieved October 20, 2011.

R

"Reactive Attachment Disorder." Mayo Clinic. http://www.mayoclinic.com/health/reactive-attachment-disorder/DS00988 Retrieved September 12, 2011.

"Recognition of the fetal alcohol syndrome in early infancy." (1978). Jones, K. L., & Smith, D. W. *Sensory, processing, perception, and behaviour*. (New York: Raven. Lancet, 2, pp 999-1001. 1973. Livingston, R. B. 1978.

"Recommended Assessment Tools for Children and Adults with confirmed or suspected FASD." (2001). Teresa Kellerman, revised 2005-10 ©. http://www.comeover.to/FAS/AssessmentsFASD.htm. Retrieved May 29, 2011.

"Relation of maternal age and pattern of pregnancy drinking to functionally significant cognitive deficit in infancy." (1998). Jacobson, J.L, Jacobson, S.W, Sokol, R.J, and Ager, J.W. (*Alcoholism: Clinical and Experimental Research* 22(2) : 345 351.

"Risk factors for adverse life outcomes in fetal alcohol syndrome and fetal alcohol effects." (2004). Streissguth, A. P., Bookstein, F. L., Barr, H., Sampson, P. D., O'Malley, K. M. B., & Kogan, J. (*Journal of Developmental and Behavioural Pediatrics*, 25, pp 228-238.

"Romberg Testing." http://en.wikipedia.org/wiki/Romberg's_test Retrieved October 2, 2011.

"Rosa's Law to remove stigmatized language from law books."(2010). Lawyer, L. Ithaca, New York: The Ithaca Journal. http://www.theithacajournal.com/article/20101126/NEWS01/11260346/Rosa+s+Law+to+remove+stigmatized+language+from+law+books Retrieved October 13, 2011.

"Rubella." http://www.nlm.nih.gov/medlineplus/ency/article/001574.htm Retrieved October 5, 2011.

S

"SECONDARY DISABILITIES AMONG ADULTS WITH FETAL ALCOHOL SPECTRUM DISORDER IN BRITISH COLUMBIA." (2004). Clark, E. Lutke, J, Minnes, P, Ouellette-Kuntz, H. FAS Int. 2004; 2:e13 Oct. 2004© The Hospital for Sick Children 2004.

"Self-centred." http://www.thefreedictionary.com/self-centred Retrieved October 23, 2011.

"Sensory Integration in diverse populations."(2008). In S. S. Roley, E. I. Blanche, & R. C. Schaaf. *San Antonio, TX: Therapy Skill Builders.* (Eds.), pp. 57-79.

"Sensory Integration Theory". Ayers, J.A. 1968. http://www.efrconline.org/admin/files/Parent'sGuideToSI.pdf Retrieved October 2, 2011.

"Sensory Integration: Theory and practice." (2002). 2nd edition. Bundy, A. C., Lane, S. J., & Murray, E. A. *Philadelphia*: F. A. Davis.

"Sensory processing in children with fetal alcohol syndrome." (1995). Morse, B. A., Miller, P. T., & Cermack, S. A. (*Alcoholism: Clinical and Experimental Research*, pp 19, 588.

"Sensory processing, school performance, and adaptive behaviour of young school-aged children with fetal alcohol spectrum disorders."(2008). Jirikowic, T. L., Olson, H. C., & Kartin, D. (in press). *Physical and Occupational Therapy in Pediatrics*.

"Sensory Profile manual." (1999). Dunn, W. San *Antonio, TX: Psychological Corporation*.

"Sexual Abuse Prevention Strategies and Programs for Persons with Developmental Disabilities." (1991). Mussigrosso, Lynne. *Sexuality and Disability*, Volume 9, Number 3. Human Sciences Press Inc. 1991.

"Smith's Recognizable Patterns of Human Malformations" (1982). Smith, David W. WB Saunders Company, Harcourt Brace Jovanovich, Inc. Philadelphia, Revised edition 1982. P.A, page 491-499.

"Some of the universal "good things of life" which the implementation of Social Role Valorization can be expected to make more accessible to devalued people." (1996). Wolfensberger, W., Thomas, S., & Caruso, G SRV/VRS: The International Social Role Valorization Journal 2(2), 12-14.

"SIDS and Overheating." Dr. Shabih Hasan, Professor in the Department of Paediatrics at the University of Calgary Faculty of Medicine. (*American Journal of Respiratory and Critical Care Medicine*. http://medicine.ucalgary.ca/about/sids retrieved June 17, (*Published in 2011-06*)

T

"Taber's Cyclopaedic Medical Dictionary." (2001). Edition 19, FAS COMPANY, Philadelphia, U.S.A, Copyright 2001, page 2152.

"Tactile defensiveness." Sensory Processing Disorder. http://www.sensory-processing-disorder.com/tactile-defensiveness.html Retrieved October 20, 2011.

"Teaching Students With Fetal Alcohol Syndrome/Effects: A Resource Guide for Teachers." Ministry of Education, Government of British Columbia, 1996. http://www.bced.gov.bc.ca/specialed/fas

The Challenge of Fetal Alcohol Syndrome: Overcoming Secondary Disabilities. (1997.) Streissguth, A., and Kanter, J., eds. Streissguth, A., and Kanter, J., eds. 1997.Seattle: University of Washington Press.Center for Adoption Medicine. University of Washington. 2005.

"The Educational Challenges Inclusion Study". Wolpert, Gloria (1996). National Down syndromeSociety. National Down syndromeSociety (Archived from the original on 2008-04-20) http://www.altonweb.com/cs/downsyndrome/index.htm?page=bosworth.html. Retrieved June 12, 2010.

"The Effects of Prenatal exposure to alcohol." (1992).Day, N.L. (*Alcohol Health and Research World*, 16(2), 328-244.

"The new genocide of handicapped & afflicted people." (2005). Wolfensberger, W (3rd (rev) ed. Syracuse, NY: Syracuse University Training Institute for Human Service Planning, Leadership & Change Agentry.

"The Out-Of-Sync Child: Recognizing and Coping With Sensory Processing Disorder". (2005).Stock Kranowitz, C. Revised 2nd edition. Perigee.

"The Sensory Profile: A discriminant analysis of children with and without disabilities." (1998). Ermer, J., & Dunn, W. *American Journal of Occupational Therapy*, pp 52, 283-290.

"Therapeutic motor training ameliorates cerebellar effects of postnatal binge alcohol." (2000). Klintsova, A.Y, Goodlett, C.R, and Greenough, W.T. (*Neurotoxicology and Teratology* 22(1) : 125 132.

"Treating hyperkinetic disorders in childhood." (1995). Taylor, E., Hemsley, R. http://scholar.google.ca/scholar?hl=en&lr=&q=related:7XJW29KM4v0J:scholar.google.com/&um=1&ie=UTF-8&ei=aHOkTpDDHczbiALn3IVX&sa=X&oi=science_links&ct=sl-related&resnum=1&ved=0CB4QzwIwAA Retrieved October 14, 2011.

"Treatment for Dysfunction in Sensory Integration." *What is sensory integration dysfunction (also called Dysfunction of Sensory Integration or DSI)*. Kelley, Kim, M.A, O.T.R, Minneapolis, MN. Down syndromeNews, Volume 26, No. 4. http://www.ndsccenter.org/resources/documents/sensoryIntegration.php Retrieved July 22, 2011.

U

"Understanding the occurrence of secondary disabilities in clients with fetal alcohol syndrome (FAS) and fetal alcohol effects (FAE)." (1996). Streissguth A, Barr H, Kogan J & Bookstein F . Final report to the Centers for Disease Control and Prevention. Grant #R04/CCR008515. Seattle: University of Washington School of Medicine.

"Understanding Sensory Integration." (2004). DiMatties, M.E. http://www.ldonline.org/article/5612/ Retrieved October 20, 2011.

"Unilateral hydronephrosis" http://www.nlm.nih.gov/medlineplus/ency/article/000506.htm Retrieved July 23, 2010.

"United Nations Office on Drugs and Crime "UNODC Executive Director visits drug treatment center in Tehran." (July 20 ,2011) http://www.unodc.org/unodc/en/frontpage/2011/July/unodc-executive-director-visits-drug-treatment-centre-in-tehran.html?ref=fs1 Retreived July23, 2011.

W

"Wechsler Intelligence Scales." http://medical-dictionary.thefreedictionary.com/Wechsler+Intelligence+Test Retrieved October 23, 2011.

"Wechsler Intelligence Scales for Children - Revised (WISC-IV)." (2008). Weschler, D.. San Antonio, Texas, U.S.A. The Psychological Corporation. Harcourt Brace and Company.

"What Advocates have said." (2001). Wolfensberger, Wolf. Published in Citizen Advocacy Forum, Vol. 11, No. 2, pp. 4-27.

"What are the characteristic features and symptoms of Down syndrome?" (1996). MedicineNet, Inc. http://www.medicinenet.com/down_syndrome/page5.htm ©1996-2011. Retrieved June 26, 2010.

Key Terms Index

About the Author

Liz Lawryk BSW MSc. Health Sciences, RSW, is currently the Chief Clinical Examiner of the **OBD** (**O**rganic **B**rain **D**ysfunction) Triage Institute, and Executive Director of the Canadian FASD Foundation. She has worked with children, youth, adults, and families within the Rehabilitation, Hospital, and Children's Services systems for nearly three decades

Her research of Fetal Alcohol Syndrome and Related Conditions began in 1989. Ms. Lawryk developed the **OBD** (Organic Brain Dysfunction) Triage Instrument and Model: A Screening Instrument for use in the Evaluation of Teratogenic Effects on Embryonic Development 1998, 2011© The model is utilized in providing the FASD diagnostic physician and team with the pertinent information required for to evaluate an accurate and responsible medical diagnosis of possible organic brain dysfunction.

As guest professor, she has co-taught the Fetal Alcohol Syndrome and Related Disability Issues course at the University of Calgary, in Alberta, Canada, and has provided training seminars and keynote lectures to hundreds of parent and professional groups including FASD Diagnostic Medical Clinic Teams, the Canadian Society of Addiction Medicine, University of Calgary, Faculty of Medicine, the Alberta Provincial Judges Association, Children's Services / Child Welfare, and Community Service Agencies, various Aboriginal Services, Justice Professionals, Federal Correctional Institutions, Pharmaceutical Associations, and School Boards.

Ms. Lawryk has been qualified as an expert witness in Fetal Alcohol Spectrum Disorders and Neonatal Abstinence Syndrome, in Youth, Family, and Provincial Courts in the Province of Alberta, Canada. She developed the Diagnostic Interpretation of Abilities Clinics ©, which provides families, support team, and agency staff with a clear explanation of the patient's respective medical diagnosis. More importantly, clinics identify how factors of the whole body disorder might translate to what appears to be wilful, defiant behaviours. Ms. Lawryk described the patient-specific concept of creative strategy development and intervention techniques with the focus on strength-based abilities in her book "Finding Perspective … Raising Successful Children Affected by Fetal Alcohol Spectrum Disorder – A Parent's Guide to Creating Prevention Strategies and Intervention Techniques." She co-edited the book, "Letters to Our Children, Letters from Our Children: Living with Fetal Alcohol Syndrome and Related Effects", authored by families living with FASDs and a contributor to a number of FASD related educational DVDs and Webinars including "FAS Forward: A Fresh Look at Fetal Alcohol Syndrome" (2001).

Her most recent book, "Adopting a Child Living with Fetal Alcohol Spectrum Disorder" addresses frequently asked questions when considering adoption or fostering a child with suspected, or a confirmed medical diagnosis within Fetal Alcohol Spectrum Disorder. Her next book, "Addictions Treatment Design for Individuals Living with Fetal Alcohol Spectrum Disorders" is due for release in the spring of 2012. Currently, Ms. Lawryk is in private practice providing Diagnostic Interpretation of Abilities Clinics ©, as well as numerous parent and professional focused seminars. She is well known for her energetic, humorous and accessible lectures, and making complex issues easy to understand.